Introduction

A WARM WELCOME!

We are excited that you are joining us for a nutrition revolution that will change your life and health forever!

This Menu Book was created for the 2016 Food Day Challenge, an annual event hosted by UC Davis Integrative Medicine and held every October–November in honor of World Food Day.

During the event, participants take steps to transition to a healthier lifestyle by following a 100 percent whole food, plant-based diet for 3 weeks.

The 2016 Challenge is complete but with this Menu Book, you can take (and repeat) the challenge at any time!

LET'S GET STARTED!

BEFORE YOU START...
Download your shopping list from the link below:
bit.ly/21fdc-2016

Before You Begin

How to Use This Menu Book

The pages you are about to read include the tools and resources you will need to adopt a whole food, plant-based diet for 21 days. We share recipes, weekly menus, shopping lists, and other tips to take you step-by-step through the world of plant-based living. Below is what you need to know to use this book during your journey.

Organization

We divided the recipes into 3 weeks, each with its own theme.

- **Week 1: Latin American Cuisine**
- **Week 2: Mediterranean Cuisine**
- **Week 3: Asian and Middle Eastern Cuisine**

You will find unique suggestions for lunches and dinners for each of the 21 days. You can try them out in order or, if you enjoy a particular recipe or theme, feel free to bring a certain recipe back! We have provided structure, but it is completely customizable to your preferences!

In addition to weekly themes and daily recipes, we have sections for:

- **Breakfasts**
- **Snacks**
- **Weekly Salads**

These parts of your weekly menu are up to you to personalize. Choose 2–3 breakfasts you would like to try for the week and eat each one on alternate days. Likewise, decide how much of the weekly salad you will incorporate into your daily meals. Finally, select your favorite fun snack ideas for when you want a treat.

Shopping and Preparation

These features will make it easier to follow the 21-Day Food Day Challenge.

1. **Shopping Lists**

   Each recipe has its own individual list to make your trip to the grocery store a breeze. Before you head out, gather lists for your favorite lunch and dinner recipes, as well as your selected breakfasts, snacks and salads.

2. **Batch Cooking**

   You will notice that we have used canned and/or frozen legumes and vegetables in recipes whenever possible to make cooking easier and quicker for you. However, we encourage you to make your own at home, and for that we have instructions in our Resources section. The guiding principle is that you can simplify your work in the kitchen with advanced preparation and by batch cooking on the weekend. For instructions, see **Advance Preparation** and **Batch Cooking** (page 91) and **How to Cook Dried Beans** (page 92) in the Resources section.

3. **Two Servings**

   We have simplified preparation by scaling all recipes down to 2 servings each to make it easier for those taking the challenge alone. If you are participating as a family or would like to have additional servings available, you can easily double (or triple!) the recipe to have enough for everyone.

....

Grocery Lists

 For your convenience, we provide grocery lists for each of the recipes as well as a general pantry list of non-perishable items which will be helpful even after the challenge is over. Please download them here: **bit.ly/21fdc-2016**

3

The Energy Density Approach

As you browse the menus and recipes, you will notice that calories per serving and other nutrition facts about the dishes are not included. The menu was purposely designed that way so that you can learn to use the Energy Density approach to healthful eating instead of counting calories. Energy density is a measure of the amount of calories in a food compared to its weight.

If you are following this challenge in an effort to lose weight, you can modify your meals and bring the energy density of many of the recipes down just by omitting or replacing ingredients marked with a red dot.

The energy density of any specific food or recipe will vary depending on its ingredients. The more water and fiber in a food, the lower its energy density, while the more fat in a food, the higher its energy density. Whole foods that are high in fat and/or natural sugars can be part of a whole food, plant-based diet and some of them are particularly health promoting — e.g. walnut, chia, flaxseed. Those high energy-dense foods are marked with a red dot throughout the Menu Book and the accompanying shopping lists.

Also, the Weekly Salads have been included in the Menu Book to help you consume foods from the lower energy density category with every lunch and dinner. It is aimed at increasing the nutrient density and 'diluting' the energy density of your meal at the same time.

Serving Size vs. Portion Size

Recipes in the Menu Book represent two servings each. They are not necessarily two portions or enough to feed two people. The difference between serving size and portion size is described below.

Serving Size: The amount of food that is typically served. For example, a serving of raw leafy green vegetables is one cup while a serving of beans is half a cup.

Portion Size: The amount of food you choose to eat at any one time. A portion is 100 percent under your control. You may eat as many servings as you wish in order to create a satiating portion. Every meal can (and should) consist of many servings of different unprocessed and/or minimally processed plant-based foods.

4

A Real World Experience

Overall, we did our best to provide a "real world" experience for you to follow a plant-based diet.

- **Customization:** The ability to choose the breakfasts that work best for your schedule and likes. You also have the option to follow the daily lunch and dinner recipes presented or repeat your favorites.

- **Simplification:** You can make your experience easier through batch cooking on the weekend and by using grocery lists.

- **Versatility:** The sharing of simple and well-loved dishes along with the use of a few key ingredients each week can help you learn how to tweak recipes and enjoy them in different ways.

Get the Support You Need

We want to be here for you every step of the way. While the 2016 Challenge may be complete, you can still connect with us on our blog, on Facebook or by email. Ask questions. Read success stories and let them motivate you. This is your journey and you are not alone. Congratulations on taking this first, important step to a plant-based lifestyle!

- UCDIM.com
- facebook.com/UCDIM
- twitter.com/UCDIM
- instagram.com/UCDIM
- pinterest.com/UCDIM

Table of Contents

Week 1 | Latin American Cuisine

	Day 1	Day 2	Day 3
Breakfast	For entire week, choose 2–3 options, to your preference, and rotate one per day from recipes on pages 10–23		
Weekly Salad	Slaw Salad	26		
Lunch	Golden Beet and Kale Salad, Corn Fritters	27	Black Bean Burrito	28	Roasted Veggie Salad	29
Snack	For entire week, choose 2–3 options, to your preference, and rotate one per day from recipes on pages 50–59		
Dinner	Black Bean Chili, Cashew Sour Cream	62	Asparagus Soup	63	Baked Potato	64 Mushroom Gravy	65

Week 2 | Mediterranean Cuisine

	Day 1	Day 2	Day 3
Breakfast	For entire week, choose 2–3 options, to your preference, and rotate one per day from recipes on pages 10–23		
Weekly Salad	Italian Salad	34		
Lunch	Summer Squash With Pesto	35	Chickpeas and Tomato Stew	36	Farmer's Market Salad	37
Snack	For entire week, choose 2–3 options, to your preference, and rotate one per day from recipes on pages 50–59		
Dinner	Fusilli Alla Puttanesca	71 Kale and Chickpea Salad	72	Roasted Garlic Mashed Cauliflower	73 Oven Roasted Autumn Vegetables	74	Vegetable Lasagna Rolls	75 Fresh Mixed Greens and Berry Salad	76

Week 3 | Asian & Middle Eastern Cuisine

	Day 1	Day 2	Day 3
Breakfast	For entire week, choose 2–3 options, to your preference, and rotate one per day from recipes on pages 10–23		
Weekly Salad	Asian Chop Salad	42		
Lunch	Banh Mi Bowl	43	Cauliflower Couscous	44	Turkish Chickpea Salad	45
Snack	For entire week, choose 2–3 options, to your preference, and rotate one per day from recipes on pages 50–59		
Dinner	Drunken Noodles	81	Moroccan Tofu	82	Five-Spice Cauliflower	83

Latin American Cuisine

Day 4	Day 5	Day 6	Day 7
For entire week, choose 2–3 options, to your preference, and rotate one per day from recipes on pages 10–23			
Slaw Salad	26			
Hummus Veggie Wrap	30	Yummy Black Bean, Beet and Shiitake Burger, Apple and Endive Salad	31	Roasted Rice and Kale Stuffed Peppers	32	Spicy Black Bean and Corn Salad	33
For entire week, choose 2–3 options, to your preference, and rotate one per day from recipes on pages 50–59			
Mango Fried Rice	66 Sautéed Brussels Sprouts With Caramelized Onions	67	Hummus Veggie Tortilla Pizza	68	Southwestern Sweet Potato Chips	69	Steamed Broccoli	70 Mushroom Gravy	65 Wholesome Power Wedges	70

Mediterranean Cuisine

Day 4	Day 5	Day 6	Day 7
For entire week, choose 2–3 options, to your preference, and rotate one per day from recipes on pages 10–23			
Italian Salad	34			
Sweet Potato Salad	38	Un-Tuna Sandwich	39	Waldorf Salad	40	Holiday Wild Rice With Cranberries and Pecans, Sautéed Spinach	41
For entire week, choose 2–3 options, to your preference, and rotate one per day from recipes on pages 50–59			
Wild Rice With Chickpeas	77	Pappa Al Pomodoro (Bread and Tomato Soup)	78	Spaghetti Squash With Roasted Garlic and Tomatoes	79	Vegan Shepherd's Pie	80

Asian & Middle Eastern Cuisine

Day 4	Day 5	Day 6	Day 7
For entire week, choose 2–3 options, to your preference, and rotate one per day from recipes on pages 10–23			
Asian Chop Salad	42			
Vietnamese-Style Spring Rolls With Baked Tofu	46	Red Cabbage and Avocado Salad	47	Spicy Peanut Tofu Lettuce Wraps	48	Baked Falafel, Tomato Cucumber Salad	49
For entire week, choose 2–3 options, to your preference, and rotate one per day from recipes on pages 50–59			
Vegetable Coconut Curry With Rice	84	Mango and Cauliflower Stir Fry	85	Soba Noodles With BBQ Tofu and Vegetables in Peanut Sauce	86	Bulgur and Lentil Pilaf With Leeks	87

Steel-Cut Oatmeal

Breakfast

Our breakfast section is designed to share ideas about the delicious, plant-based options that await you. Take a few minutes to review them and select 2–3 choices that will fit your schedule and make you look forward to eating breakfast every morning.

Recipes are listed in order, from the quickest and easiest choices to those that take a little more work or time to prepare. From nutrient-rich whole fruit to flavorful, fluffy pancakes, explore the yummy alternatives of a healthful, plant-based breakfast.

Whole Fruit

Whole fruit is a go-to food for plant-based eaters — the ideal nourishment for breakfast as well as for snacks and desserts.

Why is whole fruit such a great breakfast choice?

- **Low Energy Density:** Fruits have an energy density of 140–420 calories per pound. That means you can fill yourself up without the extra calories found in more dense foods.
- **Nutrient-Rich:** Fruits are packed with the essential nutrients your body needs, including vitamins, fiber, and antioxidants.

A serving size of fruit is about 1 cup. Here is how it works out for some popular breakfast fruits:

- **Apple:** 1 small apple, approximately 2 ¼" in diameter.
- **Banana:** 1 large banana, about 8" to 9" long.
- **Grapes:** Approximately 32 seedless grapes.
- **Orange:** 1 large orange, around 3 ¹⁄₁₆" in diameter.
- **Peach:** 1 large peach, approximately 2 ¾" in diameter.
- **Strawberries:** About 8 large berries.

Whole Grain Bread

Whole grain bread is also a popular, simple breakfast option for plant-based eaters; however, it should be noted that bread has a higher energy density than fruits, vegetables, and legumes, and it is often topped with spreads that add additional calories.

That said, whole grain bread is an acceptable breakfast, as long as you read the food label carefully before purchasing it at the store.

- **Make Sure It Is a WHOLE Grain:** In the ingredients list, look for words like "whole," "cracked," "stone ground," "sprouted," and "rolled" (example — whole grain flour, cracked wheat, and rolled oats). Avoid words that indicate refined carbs, such as white flour, bleached flour, "enriched," and "fortified."

- **Fat:** Calories from fat should be less than 20 percent of the total calories; you can calculate this by dividing calories from fat by the calories per serving.

- **Sodium:** The milligrams of sodium listed on the package should be less than the number of calories per serving.

- **Trans Fat:** There should be no trans fat in the bread you choose.

- **Cholesterol:** There should be zero cholesterol listed.

- **Added Oils:** Avoid added oils or fats including hydrogenated or partially hydrogenated vegetable oils, margarine, shortening, cocoa butter, coconut oil, palm oil, and palm kernel oil.

- **Added Sugar:** Limit any added sugars among the first 3–5 ingredients on the label, including high fructose corn syrup, sucrose, fructose, evaporated cane juice, agave, molasses, maple syrup, or concentrated fruit juice.

13

Whole Grain Cereal

Homemade Nut Milk

Whole Grain Cereal

Whole grain cereal is another breakfast choice for plant-based eaters, but, as with whole grain bread, keep in mind that this option has a higher energy density than fruits and vegetables.

The cereal can be prepared in a plant-based manner by using nut milk instead of regular dairy milk; although, once again, this is a higher energy dense breakfast than whole fruit.

When choosing a dry, whole grain cereal in the store, many of our recommendations for choosing whole grain bread apply.

- Make sure it is a whole grain by looking for words in the ingredient list like whole, cracked, stone ground, sprouted and rolled.

- Choose an option that is high in fiber, which will keep you full until lunch. Between 2 and 3 grams per serving indicates a good source of fiber, while 5 grams or higher is an excellent source.

- Watch out for added sugar. Limit any added sugar among the first 3–5 ingredients. You can always sweeten your cereal at home by adding fresh fruit.

After locating a good store-bought whole grain cereal, it is ideal to make your own nut (or grain) milk because store-bought plant milks may contain unhealthful additives too.

Plus, homemade nut milk is simple to prepare, with only two ingredients! Here is our recipe.

Homemade Nut Milk

Prep Time 10 min, Cook Time 0 min, Serves 4 cups

INGREDIENTS

4 cups water

1 cup nuts, soaked overnight •

DIRECTIONS

1. Place nuts in water to soak overnight, adding 2–3x water to make sure the nuts are submerged and will remain covered even after they increase in volume.

2. In the morning, drain the water out.

3. Add nuts and four cups water to a high speed blender and blend until smooth.

4. Pour liquid into a nut milk bag or cheesecloth fabric to allow to strain. Transfer nut milk into a glass jar. Store it in the refrigerator for up to one week.

5. Shake and serve chilled.

Apple Cinnamon Oatmeal

Prep Time 15 min, Cook Time 10 min, Serves 2

INGREDIENTS

1 cup water

⅓ cup apple, diced

⅓ cup rolled oats

2 tablespoons walnuts • (optional)

2 teaspoons maple syrup • (optional)

2 teaspoons raisins, seedless •

Cinnamon, ground, to taste

DIRECTIONS

1. In a medium saucepan, bring water to boil over medium heat.

2. Pour in oats, raisins, apple, and cinnamon, stirring continuously.

3. Reduce heat and let the mixture simmer until it reaches a smooth, creamy consistency, stirring occasionally, 7 to 9 minutes.

4. Serve in bowl with maple syrup and walnuts (optional).

Notes

You can use Homemade Nut Milk (page 14) instead of water for a creamier texture.

15

Creamy Steel-Cut Oatmeal

Prep Time 10 min, Cook Time 5 min, Serves 2

Steel-Cut Oatmeal

Fresh Berries

INGREDIENTS

2 cups water

½ cup steel-cut oats

1 ½ tablespoon maple syrup • (optional)

½ teaspoon flaxseed meal (per serving)

Fresh fruit (optional)

Homemade Nut Milk (page 14)
or store-bought plant-based milk (optional)

DIRECTIONS

1. Boil water.

2. Add oatmeal.

3. Cover pot and store overnight in refrigerator.

4. The next morning, add flaxseed and re-warm in microwave for 2 minutes.

5. Add favorite fruit, maple syrup, and plant-based milk (optional).

Notes

Steel-cut oats should be prepared ahead of time to last for a few days or even a whole week. Unlike oatmeal made with rolled oats (which becomes gluey), steel-cut oats get creamier and more delicious when reheated!

Breakfast Berry-Oatmeal Bake, Cocoa Spiced Quinoa Breakfast Bowl

Oatmeal: Prep Time 10 min, Cook Time 25 min, Serves 2 | Quinoa: Prep Time 5 min, Cook Time 30 min, Serves 2

INGREDIENTS

Oatmeal Bake

1 cup bananas, ripe, mashed

1 cup rolled oats

½ cup berries, fresh, halved

½ cup raisins, yellow or red •

2 tablespoons orange juice, freshly squeezed

2 tablespoons pecans, toasted, chopped • (optional)

2 tablespoons prunes, dried, pitted, no sugar added, chopped •

2 tablespoons walnuts, toasted, chopped • (optional)

1 teaspoon vanilla extract

Quinoa Breakfast Bowl

1 cup Homemade Nut Milk (page 14) or store-bought plant-based milk

½ cup quinoa

½ cinnamon stick

2 tablespoons cranberries, dried •

1 ½ tablespoon maple syrup •

1 tablespoon cocoa powder, unsweetened

Ginger, ground, to taste

Nutmeg, ground, to taste

DIRECTIONS FOR OATMEAL BAKE

1. Mash bananas in a large mixing bowl.

2. Add raisins, walnuts, pecans, prunes, and vanilla extract, then mix.

3. Add oatmeal and stir until well combined.

4. Layer the bottom of a glass baking dish with halved berries, then squeeze fresh orange juice over the berries.

5. Add oatmeal mixture on top.

6. Bake at 350°F for 20–25 minutes and serve while warm.

Notes

To toast walnuts and pecans, place them on baking sheet and roast at 400°F for 5–8 minutes.

DIRECTIONS FOR COCOA SPICED QUINOA BREAKFAST BOWL

1. Bring plant-based milk to a low simmer. Add all ingredients into the milk and reduce heat. Cover and cook for 20–25 minutes.

2. Remove the cinnamon stick.

3. Adjust the thickness by adding more plant-based milk, if needed.

4. Garnish with fresh fruit such as blueberries, sliced bananas, or unsweetened shaved coconut.

Quinoa Breakfast Bowl

Oatmeal Bake

Apple Pancakes

Prep Time 5–10 min, Cook Time 10 min, Serves 2

INGREDIENTS

½ cup apple, peeled, cored, chopped

¼ cup pastry flour, whole wheat
(optional: gluten-free all-
purpose baking mix)

6 tablespoons Homemade Nut Milk
(page 14) or store-bought plant-based milk

2 tablespoons apple juice, unsweetened

1 tablespoon almonds, roasted, chopped •

¾ tablespoon almond butter •

1 ½ teaspoon sucanat • (optional)

1 teaspoon baking powder

¼ teaspoon vanilla extract

DIRECTIONS

1. Preheat oven to 200°F and place a cookie sheet inside the oven.

2. Sift the flour, sucanat, and baking powder into a large bowl.

3. Combine Homemade Nut Milk, apple juice, almond butter, and vanilla extract into a food processor and blend until smooth.

4. Add enough wet ingredients into the flour mixture until the batter is moist (you will likely have leftover wet ingredients mix, which can be stored for future use). Fold in apples and almonds.

5. Heat a griddle or non-stick pan until hot.

6. Ladle about ¼ cup batter onto the griddle and cook until small bubbles appear on top of the pancakes, about 2 minutes.

7. Flip the pancakes with a spatula and cook until the second side is lightly browned, about 1 minute longer.

8. Transfer cooked pancakes onto the cookie sheet in the oven to keep warm. Repeat with the remaining batter.

Fluffy Vegan Pancakes

Prep Time 10 min, Cook Time 10 min, Serves 2

INGREDIENTS

1 cup Homemade Nut Milk (page 14) or store-bought plant-based milk

¾ cup pastry flour, whole wheat (optional: gluten-free, all-purpose baking mix)

½ cup banana, mashed

¼ cup blueberries (optional)

¼ cup rolled oats

1 tablespoon baking powder

1 tablespoon flaxseed meal

1 tablespoon maple syrup • (more to serve)

DIRECTIONS

1. Add rolled oats to a blender or food processor and blend it until flour.

2. Add whole wheat flour, baking powder, and flaxseed meal to the blender. Pulse to combine.

3. Add bananas, plant-based milk, maple syrup and mix again.

4. Stir in the blueberries.

5. Heat a non-stick griddle over medium heat.

6. Pour ¼ cup mixture onto heated griddle. Flip to turn over when bubbles start to appear on the surface of each pancake. Cook until brown on both sides. Repeat until all mixture has been used.

7. Enjoy with warm maple syrup.

Notes

Making this recipe using a high-speed blender will help clean up. In that case, add blueberries to each pancake individually.

Tofu Scramble

Prep Time 5 min, Cook Time 5 min, Serves 2

INGREDIENTS

2 cups silken tofu, extra firm, lightly pressed

½ teaspoon turmeric, ground

¼ teaspoon garlic powder

¼ teaspoon onion powder

DIRECTIONS

1. Crumble tofu into a non-stick pan, breaking it up with your fingers (a potato masher works well). Add turmeric, onion powder and garlic powder into tofu and mix well. Cook for 2 to 4 minutes or until tofu is hot throughout and most of the liquid has evaporated.

2. Serve with favorite sides and toppings, such as sliced avocado, sliced tomato, salsa, and/or hot sauce.

Notes

For those who cannot eat soy, there are commercial "vegan eggs," which can be used as a substitute for the tofu. There are several brands to choose from, but in general, "vegan eggs" are sold as powder, blended with water, and then cooked like regular eggs.

VARIATIONS

Eat your scramble with veggies for a good energy density balance!

- **Avocado:** Peel, slice, and serve on top of the scramble.
- **Bell Peppers:** Remove stem and seed then finely chop. Cook about 5 minutes then add to tofu mixture.
- **Breakfast Potatoes:** Recipe is found on page 22. Prepare and then add toward the end of cooking or serve the potatoes as a side.
- **Broccoli:** Cut about one cup into small florets and then thinly slice the stems. Add along with the tofu.
- **Carrots:** Grate one small carrot and add it toward the end of cooking.
- **Mushrooms:** Thinly slice and add along with the tofu.
- **Olives:** Chop sliced olives and add toward the end of cooking.
- **Onion:** Finely chop one small onion. Cook about 5 minutes (until translucent) then add to tofu mixture.
- **Spinach:** Chop about ½ cup spinach and add toward the end of cooking.

Brunch 'Omelet'

Prep Time 5 min, Cook Time 5 min, Serves 2

The Brunch 'Omelet' can be made using tofu OR chickpea flour. We have listed ingredients for each version, but the directions are the same.

INGREDIENTS

Tofu Omelet

1 cup silken tofu, lightly drained (not the vacuum packed kind)

¼ cup chickpea flour

1 tablespoon nutritional yeast

1 ½ teaspoon arrowroot or cornstarch

1 teaspoon garlic, fresh, minced (optional)

½ teaspoon black salt, plus extra for sprinkling (optional)

¼ teaspoon turmeric, ground

Chickpea Flour Omelet

⅔ cup chickpea flour

⅔ cup water

3 tablespoons nutritional yeast

¼ teaspoon baking soda

¼ teaspoon garlic powder

¼ teaspoon onion powder

White pepper, to taste

Filling for BOTH Versions

Your choice of vegetables, e.g. asparagus, bell peppers, broccoli, green onions, mushrooms, spinach, Swiss chard, tomatoes.

DIRECTIONS

1. Combine all ingredients.

   - For **TOFU** omelet, use a food processor, adding the ingredients in the following order: garlic, tofu, nutritional yeast, turmeric, chickpea flour, and cornstarch. Make sure to purée after each addition and scrape the bowl so everything is well combined.

   - For **CHICKPEA FLOUR** omelet, combine all dry ingredients in a bowl then add water and stir until the batter is smooth.

2. Heat a large, non-stick skillet over medium heat. Pour the batter into the pan, as if making pancakes.

3. Cook for 3–5 minutes on the first side, then flip and cook an additional minute on the other side.

4. Stuff omelet with the fillings of your choice and fold over.

5. Remove from pan and serve.

Notes

The tofu omelet will be moister and taste more like regular 'egg' omelets. Black salt is optional, but it will give the traditional 'egg' taste and smell to the omelet.

For those who cannot eat soy, there are commercial "vegan eggs," which can be used as a substitute for the tofu. There are several brands to choose from, but, in general, "vegan eggs" are sold as a powder, blended with water, and then cooked like regular eggs.

Chickpea Flour Omelet

Brunch Omelet

Roasted Breakfast Potatoes

Prep Time 15 min, Cook Time 45–60 min, Serves 2

INGREDIENTS

2 cups potatoes, diced

½ cup onion, sliced

½ cup red bell pepper, sliced

2 tablespoons parsley, fresh, chopped

½ teaspoon chili powder

½ teaspoon dill, dry

½ teaspoon garlic powder

¼ teaspoon smoked paprika

DIRECTIONS

1. Preheat the oven to 375°F.

2. Line a large baking pan with parchment paper or use a silicone baking mat.

3. Rinse the potatoes and scrub dirt off. Cut them in half, then into a large dice.

4. Add to large pot and cover with cold water. Boil for approximately 15 minutes or until just soft.

5. In a sauté pan, add onion and sauté until they turn translucent. Add red bell pepper and continue to cook until onions are caramelized and bell peppers are soft.

6. Drain potatoes and transfer to baking sheet. Add onions, bell pepper, chili powder, dill, garlic powder, and smoked paprika.

7. Roast for 30–40 minutes until crispy and golden.

8. Toss with fresh chopped parsley and extra seasoning, if desired.

Sweet Potato Hash

Prep Time 10 min, Cook Time 20 min, Serves 2

INGREDIENTS

1 ½ cup sweet potato,
diced into ¼-inch cubes

1 cup onion, coarsely chopped

¼ cup green bell pepper,
coarsely chopped

1 Roasted Garlic clove (page 73)

2 tablespoons jalapeño pepper,
minced (remove seeds for less heat)

½ teaspoon Italian seasoning

Black pepper, freshly ground, to taste

DIRECTIONS

1. Bring water to boil then add diced sweet potato.

2. Boil 5–8 minutes until cooked, then drain water and set aside.

3. Preheat heavy-bottom skillet on medium heat then add onions and peppers, sautéing until the onion is translucent. If sticking or burning occurs, add water or vegetable broth.

4. Add sweet potato, roasted garlic, Italian seasoning and black pepper.

5. Continue cooking until ingredients have browned, adding a little water as needed.

23

Lunch

Weekly Salad — Slaw Salad

Prep Time 10 min, Cook Time 0 min, Serves 2

INGREDIENTS

1 cup arugula

1 cup green cabbage, shredded

½ cup carrots, shredded

½ cup red cabbage, shredded

½ cup red onion, thinly sliced

¼ cup green bell pepper, roasted

¼ cup green onion, chopped

2 tablespoons cilantro,
fresh, chopped

1 tablespoon mint, fresh, chopped

DIRECTIONS

1. Add all salad ingredients into a large bowl and mix well.

2. Add dressing to the salad and toss.

Notes

Suggested Salad Dressing: Smoky Citrus, Citrus or Avocado (pages 94–100)

Use this weekly salad recipe to add greens to your meals (and balance out their energy density). For variation, combine ingredients in different proportions and use different dressings throughout the week. To make this salad a meal in itself, add one cup roasted sweet yellow corn (thawed if using frozen) and one cup cooked black beans (drained and rinsed).

Golden Beet and Kale Salad With Corn Fritters

Salad: Prep Time 20 min, Cook Time 0 min, Serves 2 | Corn Fritters: Prep Time 5 min, Cook Time 15 min, Serves 2

INGREDIENTS

Golden Beet and Kale Salad

2 cups kale, thinly sliced

¾ cup golden beets, peeled, shredded

½ cup carrots, peeled, shredded

½ cup red bell pepper, diced

½ cup yellow bell pepper, diced

¼ cup broccoli sprouts

¼ cup green onions, thinly sliced

¼ cup hemp seeds • (optional)

Corn Fritters

1 cup sweet yellow corn, frozen, thawed

¼ cup cornmeal

¼ cup flour, whole wheat or gluten-free

¼ cup water

2 tablespoons chives, finely chopped

2 tablespoons shallots, finely chopped

1 tablespoon garlic, fresh, chopped

Black pepper, freshly ground, to taste

DIRECTIONS FOR GOLDEN BEET AND KALE SALAD

1. Place kale, beets, carrots, green onion, hemp seeds, bell peppers, and broccoli sprouts in a large mixing container.

2. Pour dressing over kale mixture and toss until kale is well coated.

Notes

Suggested Salad Dressing: Basil Tahini (page 96)

Massaging the kale for 2 to 3 minutes will make it softer.

DIRECTIONS FOR CORN FRITTERS

1. Heat a flat griddle pan or flat plates on a panini pan to medium heat.

2. Mix ingredients in a bowl, adding the water until mixture is firm enough to scoop into balls.

3. Drop a spoonful of mixture onto the pan and flatten until fritters are ⅓-inch thick.

4. Cook on medium heat until light brown. Flip over and cook the other side.

Notes

Whole wheat flour can be used instead of gluten-free flour but you will want to use less water to make sure the mixture becomes firm.

Golden Beet and Kale Salad

Corn Fritters

Black Bean Burrito

Prep Time 5 min, Cook Time 15 min, Serves 2

INGREDIENTS

2 tortillas, whole wheat or brown rice

1 cup black beans, cooked, rinsed

½ cup avocado, halved, peeled, pitted, diced •

½ cup red onion, chopped

½ cup salsa

¼ cup sweet yellow corn, frozen, thawed

2 tablespoons cilantro, fresh, chopped

1 ½ teaspoon chili powder

DIRECTIONS

1. Preheat oven to 350°F.

2. Warm tortillas by placing them in foil and heating in the oven for 15 minutes.

3. Meanwhile, add onion and chili powder to pan. Sauté over medium heat until onion softens, about 4 minutes.

4. Reduce heat to medium-low. Add corn, beans, three tablespoons salsa and cook for 10 minutes, stirring often.

5. In a small bowl, mix 6 tablespoons salsa, avocado and cilantro.

6. Remove tortillas from the oven and fill with the black bean and corn mixture. Top with avocado salsa and one tablespoon cilantro. Roll up burrito and place seam side down on plate.

7. Serve with Slaw Salad (page 26) and/or Cashew Sour Cream (page 62).

Notes

Leftover Black Bean Chili (page 62) can be used in place of the black beans and salsa mixture.

Roasted Veggie Salad

Prep Time 15 min, Cook Time 5 min, Serves 2

INGREDIENTS

1 cup romaine lettuce

⅔ cup asparagus spears, trimmed, cut into ½-inch pieces

½ cup red bell pepper, roasted, cut into strips

¼ cup artichoke bottoms, sliced

¼ cup avocado, halved, peeled, pitted, diced

¼ cup sweet yellow corn, roasted, frozen, thawed

2 tablespoons sun-dried tomatoes, cut into strips

DIRECTIONS

1. In a grill pan over medium heat, add asparagus and artichoke bottoms. Cover the pan and cook for 2 minutes, undisturbed. Turn veggies and cover again. Add roasted red bell pepper and cook for another 2 to 3 minutes.

2. Wash, drain and cut romaine hearts. Place in a bowl.

3. Add thawed roasted corn, sun dried tomatoes and roasted vegetables (warm or cold).

4. Add diced avocado and drizzle oil-free dressing before serving.

Notes

Suggested Salad Dressing: Basic Balsamic (page 95)

Hummus Veggie Wrap

Prep Time 5 min, Cook Time 0 min, Serves 2

INGREDIENTS

4 romaine lettuce leaves, ribs cut away

2 tortillas, whole wheat or brown rice

¼ cup red bell pepper, cut into thin strips

6 tablespoons hummus, oil-free

4 tablespoons cucumber, julienned

Alfalfa or broccoli sprouts (optional)

Avocado • (optional)

Basil (optional)

Microgreens (optional)

Mint (optional)

Spinach (optional)

Tomato (optional)

DIRECTIONS

1. Cook tortillas in a skillet over medium heat for 30 seconds on each side. Tortillas can also be charred directly over the gas flame for a few seconds using tongs. Tortillas can also be warmed in the microwave (covered with a damp paper towel) for 10 seconds to make them more flexible.

2. Spread three tablespoons hummus over each tortilla.

3. Add half vegetables (including optional ingredients) to each tortilla. Add lettuce last.

4. Roll each of them up and cut in half or eat whole.

Notes

Recipes for oil-free hummus can be found on page 55.

A variety of vegetables can be used for the wrap. Remember that moist vegetables will release water and make your wrap soggy. It is fine to use some wetter vegetables (e.g. tomatoes) when combined with other toppings that are drier (e.g. green leafy vegetables, bell peppers).

Yummy Black Bean, Beet and Shiitake Burger With Apple and Endive Salad

Burger: Prep Time 45 min, Cook Time 25 min, Serves 2 | Salad: Prep Time 10 min, Cook Time 0 min, Serves 2

INGREDIENTS

Black Bean, Beet, and Shiitake Burgers

¾ cup black beans, cooked, rinsed (set liquid aside)

¾ cup shiitake mushrooms, fresh, thick stems removed

½ cup forbidden rice, cooked

4 to 6 tablespoons walnuts or pecans •

2 tablespoons beets, raw

1 ½ tablespoon aquafaba

1 ½ teaspoon stone-ground mustard

½ teaspoon smoked paprika

¼ teaspoon apple cider vinegar

Black pepper, freshly ground, to taste

Apple and Endive Salad

½ head Belgian endive, separated into leaves

1 cup apple, cored, quartered, thinly sliced

1 cup mixed greens

2 tablespoons pecans, raw, halved •

DIRECTIONS FOR BLACK BEAN, BEET, AND SHIITAKE BURGERS

1. Preheat oven to 375˚F.

2. Line a baking sheet with parchment paper.

3. Rinse black beans and transfer them to a large mixing bowl. Mash them with a fork.

4. Process walnuts (or pecans) in a food processor. Add them to the mashed black beans.

5. Process shiitake mushrooms in a food processor. Mix them with forbidden rice, beets, spices and all other ingredients.

6. Chill mixture for 15 to 30 minutes in the refrigerator to thicken. Form patties by hand.

7. Wrap patties individually to freeze, or bake patties at 375˚F for 25 minutes. Cool for 2 to 3 minutes and serve on whole grain bread.

Notes

Aquafaba is the viscous liquid in which canned legumes (e.g. chickpeas) have been cooked. Three tablespoons is equal to one egg or one egg white.

....

DIRECTIONS FOR APPLE AND ENDIVE SALAD

1. Arrange mixed greens, endives and apples on a serving dish. Add pecans.

2. Pour dressing over the salad and serve.

Notes

Suggested Salad Dressing: Orange (page 100)

Black Bean, Beet and Shiitake Burger

Apple and Endive Salad

Roasted Rice and Kale Stuffed Peppers

Prep Time 25 min, Cook Time 45 min, Serves 2

INGREDIENTS

2 bell peppers, cut in half lengthwise

1 cup brown rice, cooked

1 cup kale, chopped

¾ cup tofu, firm, cut into cubes

¾ cup tomato, seeded, finely chopped

½ cup onion, chopped

⅓ cup artichoke hearts, rinsed, chopped

⅓ cup yogurt, non-dairy, plain • (optional)

¼ cup vegetable broth, low-sodium

1 teaspoon garlic, fresh, finely chopped

Black pepper, freshly ground, to taste

DIRECTIONS

1. Preheat oven to 400°F. Line cookie sheet with parchment paper.

2. Heat pan to medium-high heat and add onion. Cook until softened then add tofu and cook until a light golden brown.

3. Add kale and artichoke hearts to the pan and continue to cook for 1 minute longer or until kale is wilted.

4. Stir in broth, tomato and garlic and cook 1 to 2 minutes.

5. Remove from heat and stir in cooked rice and non-dairy plain yogurt (if using). Season with black pepper.

6. Spoon mixture into bell pepper halves and place them onto cookie sheet with filling facing up.

7. Place cookie sheet into oven and bake 25 to 30 minutes or until bell peppers begin to soften. Remove from oven and serve warm.

Notes

For those with soy allergy or sensitivity, replace tofu with mushrooms, non-soy tempeh, or seitan.

Spicy Black Bean and Corn Salad

Prep Time 5 min, Cook Time 20 min, Serves 2

INGREDIENTS

1 cup sweet yellow corn, roasted, frozen, thawed

¾ cup salsa

½ cup black beans, cooked, rinsed

½ cup onion, diced

¼ cup avocado, halved, peeled, pitted, diced • (optional)

2 tablespoons garlic, fresh, minced

1 teaspoon cumin, ground

¼ teaspoon chili powder

DIRECTIONS

1. Add garlic, onion, cumin and chili powder to a large skillet. Cook over high heat until onions are translucent, about 4 minutes.

2. Add salsa and continue to cook, stirring every so often until most of the liquid has absorbed, about 10 minutes.

3. Reduce to medium heat. Add black beans and simmer until the beans are warm and the liquid has cooked off.

4. Stir in sweet corn and turn off heat. Spoon into serving bowls.

5. Serve with sliced avocado (optional).

Notes

The salad can be made into a tofu scramble by adding 1 cup extra firm tofu that has been pressed for an hour (Tofu can be pressed and kept in the refrigerator for 2 to 3 days to expedite preparation).

33

Weekly Salad — Italian Salad

Prep Time 10 min, Cook Time 0 min, Serves 2

INGREDIENTS

3 cups radicchio, cut into long strips

1 ½ cup Roma tomatoes, diced

1 ½ cup romaine lettuce, chopped

1 cup bell pepper, cut into strips

½ cup cucumber, thinly sliced

⅓ cup artichoke hearts, rinsed, chopped

2 tablespoons Kalamata olives, chopped •

2 tablespoons walnuts, toasted •

DIRECTIONS

1. Combine all salad ingredients in large bowl and mix.

2. Add oil-free dressing and toss.

Notes

Suggested Salad Dressing: Italian or Low-Fat Italian (page 98)

Use this weekly salad recipe to add greens to your meals (and balance out their energy density). For variation, combine ingredients in different proportions and use different dressings throughout the week.

Summer Squash With Pesto

Prep Time 15 min, Cook Time 0 min, Serves 2

INGREDIENTS

Pesto

1 cup basil, fresh, tightly packed

¼ cup pine nuts •

2 tablespoons water

1 tablespoon miso paste, light (optional)

1 teaspoon garlic, fresh, minced

Squash

4 summer squash, yellow
squash, or zucchini

DIRECTIONS FOR PESTO

1. Combine all ingredients except water in a food processor. Blend and then slowly add water until desired consistency is reached.

DIRECTIONS FOR SQUASH

1. Julienne/shred zucchini using a spiralizer, mandolin, or food processor. Remove and place in bowl.

2. Add pesto to bowl of squash. Toss then serve.

35

Chickpeas and Tomato Stew

Prep Time 5 min, Cook Time 15 min, Serves 2

INGREDIENTS

2 cups chickpeas, cooked, rinsed

1 ½ cup vegetable broth, low-sodium

1 cup artichoke hearts, rinsed, chopped

1 cup tomatoes, diced, salt-free

½ cup onion, minced

2 tablespoons basil, fresh, chopped

2 tablespoons Kalamata olives, sliced •

1 tablespoon capers

1 teaspoon garlic, fresh, minced

¼ teaspoon red pepper flakes

¼ teaspoon thyme, dry

Black pepper, freshly ground to taste

DIRECTIONS

1. Heat pan on medium-high heat. Add onions and garlic, stirring until golden brown. Add half of the broth to pan to loosen onion and garlic.

2. Add remaining ingredients and stir. Bring to a boil and then reduce heat to medium, simmering for 8–10 minutes. Serve.

Notes

This recipe is a variation of our Puttanesca sauce with the addition of chickpeas. Check our guidelines for Batch Cooking (page 89) for details.

Farmer's Market Salad

Prep Time 20 min, Cook Time 10 min, Serves 2

INGREDIENTS

2 cups pasta of choice, cooked

1 cup baby heirloom tomatoes, cut in half

1 cup zucchini, thinly sliced into half moons

½ cup peaches, fresh, firm, diced (optional)

½ cup red bell pepper, cut into thin strips

½ cup sweet yellow corn

¼ cup green onions, thinly sliced

2 tablespoons basil, fresh, chopped

Black pepper, freshly ground, to taste

DIRECTIONS

1. In a large bowl, toss together tomatoes, zucchini, bell pepper, corn, peaches (if using), green onion, and dressing. Let stand 10 minutes.

2. Add cooked pasta (warm or cold) and toss gently to coat.

3. Season with pepper to taste.

4. Transfer to a serving platter and top with basil.

Notes

Suggested Dressing: Fresh Basil (page 97)

37

Sweet Potato Salad

Prep Time 30 min, Cook Time 10 min, Serves 2

INGREDIENTS

3 cups sweet potatoes, peeled,
cut into ½-inch cubes

1 cup spinach, fresh, coarsely chopped

½ cup celery, chopped

¼ cup green onions, chopped

2 tablespoons almonds, sliced •
(plus extra for garnish)

2 tablespoons raisins •

½ teaspoon orange zest

DIRECTIONS

1. Boil cubed sweet potatoes 8–10 minutes until cooked through but still firm. Drain and rinse with cold water.

2. Add cooled sweet potatoes and all other ingredients to a large bowl. Add salad dressing then toss to coat.

3. Garnish with sliced almonds and serve.

Notes

Suggested Dressing: Cashew Curry (page 96)

38

Un-Tuna Sandwich

Prep Time 10 min, Cook Time 0 min, Serves 2

INGREDIENTS

Un-Tuna Sandwich

2 cups chickpeas, cooked, rinsed

¼ cup celery, diced

¼ cup green onions, sliced

2–3 tablespoons Cashew Cream Sauce •

2 tablespoons dill relish

2 tablespoons red bell
peppers, roasted, diced

1 tablespoon Dijon mustard

1 tablespoon dill, fresh, chopped
(or ¼ teaspoon dill, dry)

1 tablespoon lemon juice, freshly squeezed

2 teaspoons capers, chopped

2 teaspoons Old Bay seasoning

Black pepper, freshly ground, to taste

Hot sauce, to taste

Cashew Cream Sauce

2 cups cashews, raw, soaked •

1 cup Homemade Nut Milk (page 14)
or store-bought plant-based milk

2 tablespoons miso paste, light

DIRECTIONS

1. To make Cashew Cream Sauce, place cashews, miso and plant-based milk in a blender and blend on high speed until creamy. Transfer to a container and reserve.

2. Next, drain and rinse chickpeas, and add them to food processor. Pulse in 15-second bursts, scrape the sides down and repeat until the chickpeas are roughly chopped.

3. Add the chopped chickpeas to a large mixing bowl followed by all remaining ingredients. Mix well.

4. Adjust the moisture of the Un-Tuna mixture by adding more Cashew Cream Sauce. Season with freshly ground black pepper and hot sauce to taste.

5. Build into a sandwich using your favorite toppings, e.g. ALT (avocado, lettuce and tomato).

39

Waldorf Salad

Prep Time 5 min, Cook Time 0 min, Serves 2

INGREDIENTS

2 cups bibb lettuce

1 cup apple, diced

½ cup celery, diced

½ cup grapes, seedless

¼ cup parsley, fresh, chopped

¼ cup walnuts, roasted •

DIRECTIONS

1. Chop or tear lettuce into a large bowl. Add remaining ingredients.

2. Add dressing to the salad bowl and toss to coat.

Notes

Suggested Dressing: Smokey Citrus (page 100)

Holiday Wild Rice With Cranberries and Pecans, Sautéed Spinach

Rice: Prep Time 20 min, Cook Time 40 min, Serves 2 | Spinach: Prep Time 5 min, Cook Time 5 min, Serves 2

INGREDIENTS

Holiday Wild Rice

½ cup wild rice, uncooked

¼ cup butternut squash, peeled, seeded, diced

¼ cup cranberries, dried •

¼ cup pecans, toasted, chopped •

2 tablespoons orange zest

2 tablespoons shallot, diced

½ teaspoon parsley, fresh (optional)

½ teaspoon thyme, fresh

Black pepper, freshly ground, to taste

Sautéed Spinach

8 cups baby spinach leaves

1 tablespoon garlic, fresh, chopped

Black pepper, freshly ground, to taste

Lemon

DIRECTIONS FOR HOLIDAY WILD RICE

1. Heat a medium sauce pan over medium heat. Add shallot and sauté for 2 minutes. Then add the rice and the appropriate amount of water as directed on the rice package. Cover and bring to a boil.

2. Once boiling, stir and lower heat to medium-low. Cover and simmer until cooked through — follow time directed on rice package.

3. Meanwhile, preheat the oven to 450°F. Toss peeled and diced butternut squash in water then transfer it to a baking sheet. Bake in the oven for 15 minutes. Turn squash and bake for another 10 minutes. In the last 2 to 3 minutes of baking, sprinkle the pecans over it to toast.

4. Once rice and roasted acorn squash are ready, toss together with orange zest, parsley, thyme and cranberries. Add freshly ground black pepper to taste and serve at room temperature.

....

DIRECTIONS FOR SAUTÉED SPINACH

1. Rinse spinach in cold water and dry.

2. In large pot, sauté garlic for 1 minute.

3. Add spinach and pepper. Stir, then cover the pot and cook for two minutes.

4. Uncover the pot and cook on high heat for one additional minute, or until all spinach is wilted.

5. Remove from pot, top with a squeeze of lemon, and serve.

41

Weekly Salad — Asian Chop Salad

Prep Time 10 min, Cook Time 5 min, Serves 2

INGREDIENTS

2 ½ cups kale, chopped

1 cup carrots, shredded

1 cup edamame, frozen, shelled

1 cup red bell pepper, cut into strips

½ cup bean sprouts

¼ cup peanuts, roasted,
oil-free, salt-free, chopped •

2 tablespoons green onion, chopped

1 tablespoon mint, fresh, chopped

DIRECTIONS

1. Cook edamame in boiling water for 3–5 minutes. Remove and allow to cool.

2. Combine edamame with other ingredients in a large mixing bowl.

3. Add dressing as desired.

Notes

Suggested Dressing: Asian (page 95)

Use this weekly salad recipe to add greens to your meals (and balance out their energy density). For variation, combine ingredients in different proportions and use different dressings throughout the week.

Banh Mi Bowl

Prep Time 30 min, Cook Time 10 min, Serves 2

INGREDIENTS

1 cup brown rice, cooked

1 cup cabbage, shredded

1 cup kale, shredded

1 cup tofu, extra firm, cut into 2 rectangles

½ cup beans sprouts

½ cup cucumber, sliced

⅓ cup carrot, shredded

2 tablespoons radishes, sliced

DIRECTIONS

1. Drain and press the tofu for 30 minutes, then rub some dressing onto the tofu.

2. Heat a nonstick pan over medium-high heat. Place the tofu in the pan, cooking until it starts to turn light brown. Flip and cook until the other side is light brown as well.

3. Toss the cabbage, carrots and kale with the remaining dressing. Set aside.

4. Build by placing rice in a bowl, then salad on top of the rice. Add tofu to one side of the bowl with sliced radishes next to it, followed by cucumber then sprouts.

Notes

Suggested Dressing: Sweet and Spicy Asian (page 101)

For those with soy allergy or sensitivity, replace tofu with mushrooms, non-soy tempeh, or seitan.

Cauliflower Couscous

Prep Time 10 min, Cook Time 0 min, Serves 2

INGREDIENTS

3 cups cauliflower florets

¼ cup mint, fresh, chopped

¼ cup parsley, fresh, chopped

1 tablespoon lemon juice, freshly squeezed

Black pepper, freshly ground, to taste

Cumin, ground, to taste

DIRECTIONS

1. Place cauliflower florets in food processor. Pulse until fine and resembling couscous.

2. In small bowl, combine lemon juice, cumin, and black pepper.

3. Add cauliflower couscous, mint, parsley, and seasoned lemon juice to large bowl. Toss to coat. Serve or refrigerate immediately.

Turkish Chickpea Salad

Prep Time 15 min, Cook Time 0 min, Serves 2

INGREDIENTS

2 cups chickpeas, cooked, rinsed

⅔ cup Kalamata olives,
rinsed, pitted, sliced •

⅓ cup parsley, fresh, chopped

3 tablespoons onion, chopped

1 ½ tablespoon Dijon mustard

2 teaspoons red wine vinegar

1 ¼ teaspoon smoked paprika

⅔ teaspoon garlic, fresh, minced

Black pepper, freshly ground, to taste

DIRECTIONS

1. Combine Dijon mustard, red wine vinegar, garlic, paprika, and freshly ground black pepper in a small bowl and mix thoroughly.

2. Combine all other ingredients in a large mixing bowl.

3. Add the sauce into the large bowl and stir until well-coated. Serve cold.

45

Vietnamese-Style Spring Rolls With Baked Tofu

Prep Time 20 min, Cook Time 10 min, Serves 2

INGREDIENTS

Vietnamese-Style Spring Rolls

12 strips Baked Tofu (page 53),
cut 4-inches long

4 to 5 rice spring roll papers

½ cup vermicelli or thin rice noodles

¼ cup cucumber, julienned

¼ cup mint, fresh, chopped

¼ cup red bell pepper, julienned

Peanut Butter Sauce

6 to 8 tablespoons water

3 tablespoons peanut butter,
roasted, oil-free, salt-free •

1 ½ teaspoon tamari, low-sodium

Red pepper flakes, to taste (optional)

DIRECTIONS

1. Cook rice noodles according to package instructions, then drain and set aside.

2. Cut vegetables into julienne strips.

3. Prepare Peanut Butter Sauce by adding all ingredients to a high-speed blender except for the red pepper flakes. Adjust consistency to taste by adding more water. Adjust flavors as needed (with tamari and/or red pepper flakes).

4. To assemble spring rolls, pour warm–hot water into a shallow dish and immerse rice paper to soften for about 10 to 15 seconds.

5. Transfer soft rice paper to a damp cutting board and gently spread out edges.

6. Add mint leaves and julienne strips to the bottom third of the rice paper wrapper, then add a small handful of vermicelli noodles followed by 2 to 3 pieces of baked tofu on top. Fold the edges (as if you are making a burrito) and roll the wrapper until seam is sealed.

7. Place seam-side down on a serving platter and cover the spring rolls with a damp warm towel to keep them fresh. Repeat until all 4 to 5 spring rolls are done.

8. Serve them whole or cut them in half or "sushi-style" right before serving.

Notes

These spring rolls are best when eaten fresh.

For those with peanut allergies, replace peanut butter with another nut butter or sunflower seed butter. For those with soy allergy or sensitivity, replace tofu with mushrooms, non-soy tempeh, or seitan.

Red Cabbage and Avocado Salad

Prep Time 10 min, Cook Time 0 min, Serves 2

INGREDIENTS

2 cups red cabbage, shaved

½ cup avocado, slightly firm,
diced into small cubes •

2 tablespoons basil, fresh, chopped

2 tablespoons green onions, chopped

2 tablespoons mint, fresh, chopped

2 tablespoons red bell pepper, diced

Bean sprouts (to garnish)

DIRECTIONS

1. Toss cabbage, avocado, fresh herbs, and salad dressing
   in a bowl. Serve garnished with bean sprouts.

Notes

Suggested Dressing: Almond Chili or Asian (pages 94–95)

Spicy Peanut Tofu Lettuce Wraps

Prep Time 30 min, Cook Time 40 min, Serves 2

INGREDIENTS

2 bibb lettuce leaves

1 cup tofu, extra-firm

¼ cup green onions, chopped

¼ cup mint, fresh, chopped

¼ cup peanuts, roasted,
oil-free, salt-free •

2 tablespoons carrot, peeled, grated

2 tablespoons date sugar

2 tablespoons tamari, low-sodium

1 ¼ tablespoon almond butter •

¼ teaspoon chili garlic
sauce (optional)

Hoisin sauce (optional)

DIRECTIONS

1. Drain and press tofu to extract excess water.

2. Preheat oven to 400°F.

3. Cut tofu into small cubes and place on parchment-lined baking sheet. Bake for 25 minutes until dry and firm. Remove from oven and let cool.

4. In a bowl, whisk tamari, date sugar, chili garlic sauce (if using), and almond butter. Add cooled tofu to the sauce and stir to coat. Let marinate for 15 minutes.

5. Heat a medium sauté pan. Transfer tofu and cook, stirring frequently, until browned. Let cool for 15 minutes.

6. Mix tofu with shredded carrot, green onion, mint, and peanuts.

7. Serve tofu inside a bibb lettuce leaf.

Notes

For those with peanut allergies, replace peanuts with roasted cashews or sunflower seeds.

For those with soy allergy or sensitivity, replace tofu with mushrooms, non-soy tempeh, or seitan.

Baked Falafel With Tomato Cucumber Salad

Baked Falafel: Prep Time 15 min, Cook Time 30 min, Serves 2 | Salad: Prep Time 15 min, Cook Time 0 min, Serves 2

INGREDIENTS

Baked Falafel

2 cups chickpeas, cooked, rinsed (set liquid aside)

¼ cup onion, chopped

2 to 4 tablespoons parsley, fresh, loosely packed

2 tablespoons flour, whole wheat or gluten-free (optional, for binding)

1 tablespoon aquafaba

1 tablespoon lemon juice, freshly squeezed

2 teaspoons garlic, fresh, chopped

1 teaspoon baking soda

1 teaspoon coriander, ground

1 teaspoon cumin, ground

Tomato Cucumber Salad

3 cups cucumber, diced

½ cup parsley, fresh, chopped

½ cup red bell pepper, seeded, diced

½ cup Roma tomatoes, seeded, diced

¼ cup green onions, sliced

¼ cup mint, fresh, minced

2 ½ tablespoons garlic, fresh, chopped

1 tablespoon lemon juice, freshly squeezed

Black pepper, freshly ground, to taste

DIRECTIONS FOR BAKED FALAFEL

1. Preheat oven to 375°F.

2. Add all ingredients into food processor (except flour and baking soda) and pulse until mixed, adding herbs and spices as desired.

3. Add baking soda (and flour, if desired) then continue pulsing until mixture begins to form a ball.

4. Scoop out the dough with your hands. Form it into large balls and add to a baking sheet, then press the balls down to make into patties that are about ½-inch thick.

5. Bake 25–30 minutes, flipping halfway through.

6. Remove from oven and serve with Tahini Dressing (page 101, optional) and Tomato Cucumber Salad.

....

DIRECTIONS FOR TOMATO CUCUMBER SALAD

1. Add all ingredients into a bowl, then drizzle with lemon juice, sprinkle with pepper, and toss to coat.

Notes

Suggested Dressing: Almond Chili or Asian (pages 94–95)

This is a quick and easy falafel recipe made with canned chickpeas; however, traditional falafels are made with dried chickpeas, which are soaked in water, overnight. Aquafaba is the viscous liquid in which canned legumes (e.g. chickpeas) have been cooked. Three tablespoons is equal to one egg or one egg white.

Baked Falafel

Tomato Cucumber Salad

Snacks

As you follow a plant-based lifestyle during our 21-Day Food Challenge, you will likely be surprised about how satisfying and fulfilling the meals are. This is because you are feeding yourself with the right type of foods and nutrients. That said, you may want a little something extra between meals. And that is okay — snacking is allowed on a plant-based diet!

Having your favorites on hand will allow you to grab a healthful and nutritious snack when you get a craving between meals.

In general, your best snack options are fruits and vegetables in their whole, natural, and unprocessed form. But you can also 'spice them up' with a delicious spread and/or add them to an open-faced sandwich.

Remember that a small portion of any food can be eaten as a snack, and that includes leftovers! To make it easier, we compiled a list of some special plant-based snacks for you to try during the challenge. And some of them can be eaten as desserts too.

Take a few minutes to review them and select 2–3 choices that sound the most delicious to you to enjoy when needed throughout the week.

You are going to love these yummy indulgences!

Air Popped Popcorn

Prep Time 5 min, Cook Time 5 min, Serves 2

INGREDIENTS

2 tablespoons popcorn kernels

DIRECTIONS

STOVE

1. Preheat a burner to medium-high heat.

2. Add kernels to a large pot. Place cover on top.

3. Place the pot on the stove. Grab handles (using a hand towel or pot holder if the handles are not heat resistant) and shake the pot lightly so kernels do not stick to the bottom.

4. Popcorn will begin to pop within seconds. Shake the pot lightly every 3–5 seconds as kernels continue to pop.

5. Remove from stove when there is a 1–2 second pause between new pops.

COMMERCIAL POPCORN POPPER

1. Commercial popcorn poppers are relatively inexpensive. Look for one that uses hot air and pops corn kernels without oil. Follow instructions to prepare.

MICROWAVE

1. Make sure to find a microwave brand that has no oil or salt added. Follow directions on package to prepare.

Baked Tofu

Prep Time 130 min, Cook Time 40 min, Serves 2

INGREDIENTS

2 cups tofu, extra firm, pressed

½ cup water

3 tablespoons tamari, low-sodium

2 tablespoons maple syrup •

1 teaspoon liquid smoke,
hickory flavor

DIRECTIONS

1. Cut tofu into ½ to 1-inch sized chunks. Place in a sealable plastic bag or glass container with lid.

2. Mix water, tamari, maple syrup, and liquid smoke in a small bowl.

3. Pour mixture over tofu and place container in refrigerator. Allow tofu to marinate for 1 to 2 hours (or overnight).

4. Flip halfway through to make sure the tofu is evenly marinated.

5. Preheat oven to 400°F.

6. Line a baking sheet with parchment paper.

7. Evenly space tofu on the cooking sheet. Bake for 20 minutes then flip tofu over and bake for another 20 minutes. Tofu should be golden brown.

8. Remove from oven and allow tofu to cool.

Notes

The marinade also works for mushrooms, which can be grilled or cooked on a griddle pan on the stove. Sliced shiitake mushrooms are particularly tasty prepared this way.

For those with soy allergy or sensitivity, replace tofu with mushrooms, non-soy tempeh, or seitan.

Crudités With Spreads

Baba Ganoush: Prep Time 30 min, Cook Time 15–20 min, Serves 2
Muhammara: Prep Time 10 min, Cook Time 10–20 min, Serves 2

Baba Ganoush

Muhammara

INGREDIENTS

Baba Ganoush

2 cups eggplant

2 tablespoons lemon juice, freshly squeezed

1 tablespoon tahini • (optional)

1–2 teaspoon garlic, fresh, minced

Muhammara

1 red bell pepper, freshly roasted

¾ cup walnuts, chopped •

½ cup green onions, chopped

3 teaspoons pomegranate molasses •

1 teaspoon Aleppo pepper flakes

1 teaspoon cumin, ground

1 teaspoon lemon juice, freshly squeezed

DIRECTIONS FOR BABA GANOUSH

1. Turn stove onto medium-low and char eggplant directly over the flame, using tongs to turn often. Cook until eggplant skin is completely charred and the flesh inside is tender.

2. Transfer eggplant to a bowl. Cover and let it "sweat" for 15 minutes.

3. Once cooled, cut eggplant in half and peel off the charred skin (or scoop out the inside). Add the flesh only to the food processor.

4. Add the remaining ingredients and blend.

5. Serve with raw vegetables, whole wheat pita bread, or rice crackers.

Notes

To decrease fat content, substitute water for tahini.

. . . .

DIRECTIONS FOR MUHAMMARA

1. To roast red bell pepper, char it on all sides directly over the flame of a gas stove. You can also roast it at 400°F until it has blistered all over. Once cooled, peel off the skin, remove the stem and seeds, and then chop.

2. Add the roasted red pepper, green onions, 2 tablespoons of pomegranate molasses, lemon juice, cumin and ½ teaspoon of Aleppo pepper flakes to a food processor and blend until smooth.

3. Stir in chopped walnuts.

4. Remove from the food processor. Place into a bowl and make a well in the center. Add the remaining one tablespoon of pomegranate molasses and ½ teaspoon Aleppo pepper flakes to the center of the well. Serve.

54

Crudites With Spreads

Prep Time 5 min, Cook Time 0 min, Makes 2–3 cups

INGREDIENTS

Classic Hummus

4 cups chickpeas, cooked, rinsed (set liquid aside)

⅓ cup tahini •

6 tablespoons lemon juice, freshly squeezed

2 to 3 tablespoons aquafaba

2 teaspoons garlic, fresh, minced

Variation 1: Harrisa and Mint Hummus

1 Classic Hummus Recipe

1 tablespoon harrisa

Mint, fresh, chopped (to garnish)

Variation 2: Artichoke and Rosemary Hummus

1 Classic Hummus Recipe

½ cup artichoke hearts, rinsed, chopped

Rosemary, fresh, chopped (to garnish)

Variation 3: Spicy Hummus

1 Classic Hummus Recipe

1 tablespoon cumin, ground

1 teaspoon smoked chipotle powder

Variation 4: Sweet Potato Hummus

1 sweet potato, cooked

2 cups chickpeas, cooked, rinsed (set liquid aside)

½ cup aquafaba

2 tablespoons lemon juice, freshly squeezed

1 teaspoon chili powder

1 teaspoon garlic, fresh, minced

¼ teaspoon tahini •

Variation 5: Sun Dried Tomato Hummus

4 cups chickpeas, cooked, rinsed (set liquid aside)

½ cup sun-dried tomato purée

⅓ cup tahini •

6 tablespoons lemon juice, freshly squeezed

2 to 3 tablespoons aquafaba

2 teaspoons garlic, fresh, minced

....

DIRECTIONS

1. Mince the garlic to a fine paste.
2. In a food processor, add chickpeas and tahini. Start by pulsing a few times then scrape the sides down.
3. Add remaining ingredients and purée. Adjust consistency with aquafaba until smooth.

Notes

To decrease fat content, use less tahini (e.g. 1 to 2 tablespoons) or substitute water for tahini.

55

Sweet and Tart Baked Apples

Prep Time 15 min, Cook Time 35 min, Serves 2

INGREDIENTS

1 apple

¼ cup water

1 tablespoon Homemade
Nut Milk (page 14) or
store-bought plant-based milk

1 tablespoon maple syrup •

1 tablespoon Medjool date,
finely chopped •

1 tablespoon rolled oats

1 tablespoon walnuts or pecans,
finely chopped •

Cinnamon, ground, to taste

Nutmeg, ground, to taste

DIRECTIONS

1. Preheat oven to 375°F.

2. Wash and slice apple in half, along core. Scoop out the core with a melon baller or spoon.

3. In a small bowl, mix maple syrup, nuts, chopped dates, oats, cinnamon, nutmeg and plant-based milk until oats are moist and mixture is crumbly.

4. Spoon one heaping tablespoon into the core of each apple half and place in a glass-baking dish.

5. Pour 1 cup of water around the apples. Cover in foil and bake for 20 minutes.

6. Remove foil and baste apples with juices from the pan. Continue to bake, uncovered, for an additional 10–15 minutes, or until apples are tender but not mushy.

Baked Pear Crisp

Prep Time 15 min, Cook Time 30 min, Serves 2

INGREDIENTS

2 pears, peeled, cored, divided

⅔ cup rolled oats

1 Medjool date, pitted, soaked
in warm water for an hour •

3 tablespoons raisins, soaked
in warm water for an hour •

1 ½ teaspoon lemon juice,
freshly squeezed

⅔ teaspoon lemon zest, finely grated

¼ teaspoon vanilla extract (optional)

Cinnamon, ground, to taste

DIRECTIONS

1. Preheat oven to 375°F.
2. Thinly slice 1 ½ pears.
3. Place sliced pears and lemon zest in a large bowl and toss.
   Set aside until step 7.
4. Chop the remaining ½ pear.
5. Drain raisins, reserving the liquid for the next step.
6. Add chopped pear, drained raisins, lemon juice and vanilla extract
   to a blender. Blend until smooth, then add a few tablespoons of
   the raisin liquid and blend until you have a purée.
7. Pour the mixture into the bowl of sliced pears (step 2 above).
8. Scrape contents of bowl into a small casserole dish or glass
   baking dish and smooth the top.
9. Drain and add dates, oats, and cinnamon to a food processor.
   Pulse until finely chopped then spread over the pear mixture.
10. Bake until the filling is bubbling and the top is browned,
    about 25 to 30 minutes. Serve warm or at room temperature.

Chocolate Ginger Chia Pudding

Prep Time 135 min, Cook Time 15 min, Serves 2

INGREDIENTS

1 cup Homemade Nut Milk (page 14) or store-bought plant-based milk

¼ to ⅓ cup Medjool dates, pitted •

½ cinnamon stick

2 tablespoons chia seeds •

2 tablespoons cocoa powder, unsweetened

Ginger, ground, to taste

Turmeric, ground, to taste

DIRECTIONS

1. Bring plant-based milk to a low simmer.

2. Add unsweetened cocoa powder, ginger, cinnamon stick, turmeric and dates into milk. Bring to a simmer. Continue to stir until ginger and turmeric are dissolved thoroughly.

3. Remove from heat. Remove cinnamon stick and allow to cool.

4. Once cool, add chia seeds. Cover and place in the refrigerator for 2 hours or overnight.

5. Pour the mixture into a blender and purée until smooth.

6. At this time, adjust sweetness by adding another ½ to 1 date.

7. Once puréed, pour into a glass and place back in the fridge to set up.

8. Serve with preferred toppings — e.g. sliced strawberries or bananas.

Chocolate Ginger Chia Pudding

Dinner

Black Bean Chili and Cashew Sour Cream

Prep Time 10 min, Cook Time 25 min, Serves 2

INGREDIENTS

Black Bean Chili

1 ½ cup sweet potato, chopped into bite-size pieces

1 cup black beans, cooked, rinsed

¾ cup salsa, chunky

⅔ cup vegetable broth, low-sodium

⅔ cup water

⅓ cup onion, diced

1 teaspoon chili powder (optional)

½ teaspoon cumin, ground (optional)

Avocado, sliced • (optional)

Chipotle powder, to taste (optional)

Cilantro, fresh (optional)

Cashew Sour Cream

½ cup cashews, raw, soaked overnight •

¼ cup water

2 teaspoons lemon juice, freshly squeezed

½ teaspoon apple cider vinegar

DIRECTIONS

1. Start on the chili by adding onions to a large pot. Cook over medium heat until they become soft and translucent.

2. Add cumin and your choice of optional spices and cook for 3 minutes.

3. Add vegetable broth, water, and salsa and increase heat to medium-high. Bring to a boil then reduce heat to medium-low.

4. Add black beans and sweet potatoes. Cover pot and continue to simmer for 20 minutes.

5. To make Cashew Sour Cream, place cashews in the blender with the other ingredients. If using a high-speed blender, use the sauce setting for a smooth cream. Chill it before serving.

6. Serve with fresh cilantro, avocado, and/or Cashew Sour Cream.

Notes

For a smoky taste you can add an oil-free plant-based 'bacon' such as seitan or tempeh bacon, or Baked Tofu (page 53) or mushrooms.

Cashew Sour Cream can be prepared ahead of time and stored in the refrigerator. If you forget to soak the cashews overnight (or between 4 to 8 hours), you can soak them for one hour in hot water and prepare while black beans are simmering.

Asparagus Soup

Prep Time 5 min, Cook Time 20 min, Serves 2

INGREDIENTS

1 cup asparagus, trimmed, cut into ½-inch pieces

1 cup vegetable broth, low-sodium

½ cup leeks, chopped

½ cup water

½ teaspoon dill, fresh, chopped (optional)

½ teaspoon fennel, fresh, chopped (optional)

½ teaspoon thyme, fresh, chopped (optional)

Black pepper, freshly ground, to taste

Parsley, fresh, chopped

DIRECTIONS

1. Heat stove to medium-high heat. Add asparagus, leeks, plus any optional spices (fennel, thyme, dill). Simmer for 4 to 5 minutes.

2. Add the vegetable broth and water. Bring to a boil then reduce heat to medium-low. Simmer for 10 to 12 minutes.

3. Add soup to the blender and blend until smooth. Season to taste with freshly ground black pepper.

4. Add to individual serving bowl and garnish with chopped parsley.

Notes

This recipe can be made using ½ large head of broccoli instead of the asparagus. In step 2 you will have to simmer the soup longer to make sure the broccoli is cooked.

For a creamier soup, you can add a tablespoon of Cashew Cream Sauce (page 39).

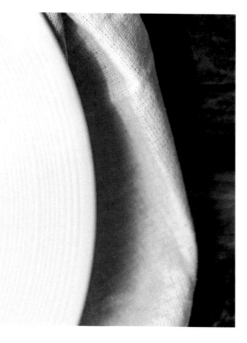

Baked Potato and Mushroom Gravy

Prep Time 5 min, Cook Time 60 min, Serves 2

Baked Potato

Mushroom Gravy

INGREDIENTS

Baked Potato

2 russet potatoes, whole

DIRECTIONS

OVEN

1. Heat oven to 350°F.
2. Wash potatoes, then poke 8–12 holes all around using a fork. This will allow the moisture to escape while cooking.
3. Place potato directly on the middle rack of the oven.
4. Bake 1 hour or until the flesh feels soft but the skin is crisp.

MICROWAVE

1. Wash potatoes, then poke 8–12 holes all around using a fork.
2. Put potatoes in a microwave-safe dish.
3. Heat on full power for 5 minutes.
4. Turn potatoes over and heat for an additional 3 to 5 minutes.
5. Continue to microwave in one minute intervals until the potatoes are cooked through.

SLOW COOKER

1. Wash potatoes, then poke 8–12 holes all around using a fork.
2. Wrap each potato in foil.
3. Place potatoes in the bottom of the slow cooker.
4. Place lid on and cook on low for 8 to 10 hours.

Notes

Baked potatoes can be paired with Mushroom Gravy or leftover Black Bean Chili (page 62, with or without Cashew Sour Cream). They can also be paired with steamed vegetables and drizzled with an with an Oil-Free Salad Dressing (pages 93–100).

Mushroom Gravy

Prep Time 5 min, Cook Time 25 min, Serves 2

INGREDIENTS

Mushroom Gravy

1 cup Homemade Nut Milk (page 14)
or store-bought plant-based milk

1 cup mushrooms, chopped

½ cup onion, chopped

1 ½ teaspoon tamari, low-sodium

1 ½ teaspoon tomato paste

¾ teaspoon maple syrup •

½ teaspoon garlic, fresh, minced

Black pepper, freshly ground, to taste

DIRECTIONS

1. Sauté mushrooms and onions in a nonstick skillet over medium heat for 5–10 minutes.

2. Add tamari, tomato paste, maple syrup, garlic and black pepper. Cook for 2 minutes.

3. Whisk in nut milk and cook for 10–15 minutes or until thickened.

21 Food Day Challenge Recipe Book | © The Regents of the University of California, Davis campus IPHI, 2017. All rights reserved | ucdim.com

Mango Fried Rice

Fried Rice: Prep Time 30 min, Cook Time 25 min, Serves 2

INGREDIENTS

3 cups rice, basmati or brown, cooked

1 cup mango, peeled, sliced into ½-inch pieces

¾ cup green beans, sliced into 1-inch pieces

½ cup onion, diced

½ cup tomato, cut into ½-inch pieces

⅓ cup cashews, raw •

1 ½ tablespoon tamari, low-sodium

1 tablespoon lime juice, freshly squeezed

1 ½ teaspoon garlic, fresh, minced

1 ½ teaspoon ginger, fresh, minced

1 ½ teaspoon hot sauce

1 teaspoon coriander seed, crushed (optional)

Red pepper flakes, to taste

DIRECTIONS

1. Preheat a large heavy bottomed pan over medium heat. Toss in the cashews and dry toast them for about 5 minutes, flipping occasionally until they are slightly browned in some spots. Transfer to a large plate.

2. Turn the heat on the pan up to medium-high. Add the green beans and a scant amount of water. Cook for 3 to 5 minutes, or until the beans are bright green and seared. Transfer beans to the same plate as the cashews.

3. Add the onions to the pan along with another tablespoon or two of water. Toss for about 3 minutes, or until they are slightly charred but still firm. Add the garlic, ginger, coriander (if using) and red pepper flakes, and toss for 30 seconds or so, being careful not to burn.

4. Add another tablespoon or two of water and about half of the cold, cooked rice. Toss to coat, then add in the remaining rice, tossing once again. Cook for about 3 minutes, tossing often, until warmed through.

5. Add the tamari, hot sauce and tomato, and toss. Cook for another 3 minutes, or until the rice has browned sufficiently and the tomato is slightly broken down.

6. Add the green beans, cashews, mangoes and lime juice. Cook just until mangoes are heated through, a minute or two.

7. Serve.

Sautéed Brussels Sprouts With Caramelized Onions

Brussel Sprouts: Prep Time 15 min, Cook Time 20 min, Serves 2

INGREDIENTS

3 cups Brussels sprouts, fresh, sliced in half

1 cup onion, chopped

2 tablespoons sesame seeds •

Pecans, for garnish • (optional)

DIRECTIONS

1. Heat a heavy skillet over medium-high heat, add sesame seeds and toast for about 3 to 5 minutes, or until golden brown and fragrant. Remove from pan and set aside.

2. Add 1 tablespoon water and onions to hot pan and cook until caramelized — soft and nicely browned around the edges. Remove onions and set aside.

3. Add 1 tablespoon water to hot pan and then add Brussels sprouts, placing them face down. Cook for 7 to 9 minutes, adding a splash of water to help the caramelizing process at the very end.

4. Remove Brussels sprouts and place in a large bowl. Add caramelized onions and toasted sesame seeds, then toss and serve.

Hummus Veggie Tortilla Pizza

Prep Time 20 min, Cook Time 15 min, Serves 2

INGREDIENTS

2 tortillas, whole wheat or brown rice

1 cup hummus, oil-free

1 cup spinach

½ cup portabella mushroom, sliced

½ cup red bell pepper, sliced

½ cup summer squash, thinly
sliced lengthwise

½ cup vegetable broth, low-sodium

¼ cup pine nuts or almonds • (optional)

3 tablespoons balsamic vinegar

Basil, fresh (optional)

Black pepper, freshly ground, to taste

DIRECTIONS

1. Add ½ cup hummus, vegetable broth and balsamic vinegar to a bowl and stir to make a marinade.

2. Place summer squash, red bell pepper and mushroom slices into the marinade and let sit for 5 to 60 minutes (the longer it sits, the more flavor will be absorbed).

3. Remove vegetables from the marinade and place on a grill pan. Grill a few minutes on each side, until you start to see nice grill marks, then remove from the heat.

4. Lightly steam the spinach then set aside.

5. Place tortillas on a baking sheet and then spread ¼ cup hummus on each.

6. Layer with grilled vegetables, then steamed spinach, then whole leaves of basil (if using), then sprinkle on the pine nuts or almonds (if using).

7. Bake at 375°F for about 15 minutes, or until the edges of the tortilla are a little crispy and the pine nuts/almonds are golden.

8. Sprinkle with freshly ground pepper and serve.

Notes

Recipes for oil-free hummus can be found on page 55.

Southwestern Sweet Potato Chips

Prep Time 15 min, Cook Time 30 min, Serves 2

INGREDIENTS

2 sweet potatoes, sliced ¼-inch thick

1 cup refried beans, oil-free

½ cup salsa (optional)

½ cup sweet yellow corn, roasted (optional)

½ cup tomato, chopped

¼ cup cilantro, fresh, chopped (optional)

¼ cup green onion, chopped

¼ cup Kalamata olives, chopped • (optional)

Smoked paprika, to taste

DIRECTIONS

1. Preheat oven to 450°F.

2. Place sweet potato slices in a single layer on a nonstick baking sheet. Sprinkle with smoked paprika and bake 30–35 minutes, flipping half way.

3. Heat refried beans.

4. Place chips on a plate and top with remaining ingredients.

Notes

Black beans can be used instead of refried beans. Cashew Sour Cream (page 62) can be added to nachos.

69

Steamed Broccoli, Mushroom Gravy and Wholesome Power Wedges

Broccoli: Prep Time 5 min, Cook Time 5, Serves 2 | Wedges: Prep Time 5 min, Cook Time 40, Serves 2

Wholesome Power Wedges

Steamed Broccoli

INGREDIENTS

Steamed Broccoli

3 cups broccoli florets

Black pepper, freshly ground (optional)

Seasoned rice vinegar (optional)

Wholesome Power Wedges

4 potatoes, cut into wedges

1 ½ teaspoon flour, whole wheat or gluten-free

½ teaspoon chili powder

½ teaspoon garlic powder

½ teaspoon onion powder

½ teaspoon smoked paprika

Black pepper, freshly ground, to taste

Mushroom Gravy

Ingredients and directions can be found on **page 65**

DIRECTIONS FOR STEAMED BROCCOLI

1. Cut off the lower third of the broccoli stem.

2. Peel the remaining stem, then cut into ½-inch thick slices.

3. Cut broccoli florets into 2-inch sections.

4. Add water to steamer. Once boiling, add broccoli and cook covered for 5 minutes or until crisp and tender.

5. Remove from steamer. Eat as-is, or toss with your choice of the optional ingredients.

Notes

Suggested Dressing: Basic Balsamic (page 95)

Frozen broccoli can be used instead of the fresh vegetable.

DIRECTIONS FOR WHOLESOME POWER WEDGES

1. Scrub and slice potatoes into ¾-inch to 1-inch thick wedges.

2. Steam potatoes in a pot for 15 minutes.

3. Preheat convection oven to 400°F (425°F for regular oven). Line a baking pan with parchment paper.

4. In a large bowl, combine all seasonings and mix. Slowly add steamed potatoes to seasoned mix and coat potatoes evenly.

5. Spread potatoes on parchment paper and bake for 25 minutes.

6. Remove from oven and serve.

Notes

Seasoning mix can be prepared in advance and stored with other spices.

Fusilli Alla Puttanesca

Prep Time 10 min, Cook Time 15 min, Serves 2

INGREDIENTS

1 ½ cup vegetable broth, low-sodium

1 cup artichoke hearts, rinsed, chopped

1 cup pasta of choice, uncooked

1 cup tomatoes, diced, salt-free

¼ cup onion, minced

2 tablespoons Kalamata olives, sliced •

1 tablespoon capers

1 teaspoon garlic, fresh, minced

½ teaspoon basil, dry

¼ teaspoon red pepper flakes

¼ teaspoon thyme, dry

Black pepper, freshly ground, to taste

DIRECTIONS

1. Bring water to boil and add pasta. Cook for 2 minutes. Turn off heat and let pasta cook in water for another 12 to 15 minutes. Drain pasta and set aside.

2. Heat pan on medium-high heat. Add onions and garlic, stirring until golden brown. Add half the broth to pan to loosen onion and garlic and then add remaining ingredients.

3. Bring ingredients to a boil then reduce heat to medium. Cover the pan and let simmer for 8 to 10 minutes. Add pasta and stir. Serve with basil, thyme, and black pepper.

Notes

This recipe can be prepared four different ways. Check our guidelines for Batch Cooking (page 89) for details.

Use fire-roasted diced tomatoes for a smokier variation.

MEAL PLAN CONTINUED ON NEXT PAGE

Kale and Chickpea Salad

Salad: Prep Time 10 min, Cook Time 0 min, Serves 2

INGREDIENTS

4 cups leafy greens of
choice, chopped

½ cup avocado, diced •

½ cup chickpeas, cooked, rinsed

Lemon slices, for garnish

DIRECTIONS

1. Toss greens, chickpeas, avocado and dressing in a large bowl.
   Serve plated with lemon slices to garnish.

Notes

Suggested Dressing: Maple Tahini, Low-Fat Italian or Fresh Basil
(pages 97–98)

72

Roasted Garlic Mashed Cauliflower

Prep Time 20 min, Cook Time 50 min, Serves 2

INGREDIENTS

Roasted Garlic Mashed Cauliflower

2 cups cauliflower florets

1 ½ to 2 cloves Roasted Garlic

1 ½ teaspoon cream cheese, dairy-free • (optional)

1 ½ teaspoon Homemade Nut Milk (page 14) or store bought plant-based milk

Black pepper, freshly ground, to taste

Chives, fresh, chopped

Roasted Garlic

2 heads garlic

2 tablespoons vegetable broth, low-sodium

Black pepper, freshly ground, to taste

DIRECTIONS FOR ROASTED GARLIC MASHED CAULIFLOWER

1. Prepare Roasted Garlic.

2. In a steamer or saucepan with a steaming rack, steam cauliflower for 10 minutes or until tender.

3. Place half the cauliflower into a food processor and blend on high until smooth. Add remaining cauliflower florets, roasted garlic, dairy-free cream cheese, nut milk, and freshly ground black pepper and blend until smooth.

4. Add chopped chives to garnish.

....

DIRECTIONS FOR ROASTED GARLIC

1. Preheat the oven to 400°F. Peel off the loose garlic skin.

2. Cut off the head so the garlic is exposed at the top.

3. Wrap the garlic heads individually in tinfoil (cut side up), adding vegetable broth and freshly ground black pepper before closing it. Place tin foil 'cups' in baking dish.

4. Roast them in the oven for 30 to 40 minutes until the cloves are golden brown.

5. Remove from oven and allow to cool for 10 to 15 minutes. Gently squeeze garlic out of each skin or use a paring knife to cut each piece away. Garlic can be mashed or served with a knife to spread on bread.

....

MEAL PLAN CONTINUED ON NEXT PAGE

Oven Roasted Autumn Vegetables

Prep Time 10 min, Cook Time 45 min, Serves 2

INGREDIENTS

1 ⅓ cup Brussels sprouts, cut in half

1 cup acorn squash, peeled, diced

⅓ cup Medjool dates, chopped •

⅓ cup pecans, chopped •

4 teaspoons apple cider vinegar

2 teaspoons Dijon mustard

1 teaspoon garlic, fresh, minced

Black pepper, freshly ground, to taste

Cinnamon, ground, to taste

Nutmeg, ground, to taste

Red pepper flakes, to taste

DIRECTIONS

1. Set oven to 375°F.

2. Combine Brussels sprouts, acorn squash, pecans and dates in a large mixing bowl.

3. In a smaller mixing bowl, combine vinegar, mustard, black pepper, cinnamon, chili flakes and nutmeg, then whisk.

4. Add content from smaller bowl into the larger bowl of vegetables and mix until well coated.

5. Line a baking sheet with parchment and transfer the glazed vegetables onto the pan.

6. Bake for 40 to 45 minutes or until vegetables are tender.

Vegetable Lasagna Rolls

Prep Time 30 min, Cook Time 45 min, Serves 2

INGREDIENTS

6 lasagna sheets, whole wheat or gluten-free

1 globe eggplant, sliced into 6 slices lengthwise

2 cups baby spinach

2 cups tomato sauce

1 ½ cup tofu, firm, pressed for 20 minutes

¼ cup red bell pepper, roasted, cut in strips

½ lemon, fresh, juiced, zested

4 tablespoons basil, fresh, chopped

2 tablespoons nutritional yeast

1 to 2 tablespoons water

1 tablespoon miso paste, light

1 teaspoon garlic powder

½ teaspoon onion powder

½ teaspoon smoked paprika

Notes

For those with soy allergy or sensitivity, replace tofu with cashews

....

MEAL PLAN CONTINUED ON NEXT PAGE

DIRECTIONS

1. Preheat oven to 400°F.

2. Bring water to boil (to cook lasagna sheets).

3. Line two baking sheets with parchment paper and lay sliced eggplant on them.

4. In a small mixing bowl combine the miso, ½ teaspoon garlic powder, paprika, 2 tablespoons basil, and water. Using your fingers, spread a thin layer onto each eggplant slice. Place in the oven, cooking for 10 to 12 minutes. Cook just until the edges start to turn light brown.

5. Place the lasagna noodles into the boiling water. Reduce the heat to a rolling simmer and stir. Cook until the noodles are al dente. (It is always best to follow the package instructions). Once cooked, drain and rinse. Set the noodles and the eggplant aside.

6. Place tofu, lemon juice, lemon zest, ½ teaspoon garlic powder, onion powder, and nutritional yeast in a food processor. Pulse to start combining tofu, scrape the side down and pulse again. Remove tofu from the food processor and place into a large bowl.

7. Spread the spinach on a lined baking sheet and place in the oven. Cook for about 2 to 3 minutes, until the spinach wilts. Roughly chop the spinach and red peppers.

8. Add the spinach, peppers and 2 tablespoons basil to the tofu. Gently fold until well combined. Pour about ½ cup of tomato sauce into your oven-proof baking dish, spread evenly.

9. On a cutting board place the lasagna sheet down, place the eggplant on top, then add a generous scoop of the tofu filling at the end of each lasagna sheet and roll up. Place the seam side down in a baking dish and repeat until all ingredients are rolled up.

10. Spoon more sauce over the lasagna rolls and bake at 375°F degrees for 20 to 25 minutes.

75

Fresh Mixed Greens and Berry Salad

Prep Time 15 min, Cook Time 10 min, Serves 2

INGREDIENTS

3 cups spinach and baby greens

½ cup blueberries

½ cup strawberries, sliced

¼ cup walnuts or pecans, chopped • (optional)

DIRECTIONS

1. If using nuts, preheat oven to 350°F.

2. Toast nuts by placing them on a baking sheet and cooking for about 10 minutes or until fragrant.

3. Remove nuts and allow them to cool.

4. Combine greens, strawberries, blueberries, and nuts in a large bowl.

5. Toss with your choice of dressing.

Notes

Suggested Dressing: Basic Balsamic (page 94)

Wild Rice With Chickpeas

Prep Time 15 min, Cook Time 15 min, Serves 2

INGREDIENTS

2 cups chickpeas, cooked, rinsed

1 ½ cup vegetable broth, low-sodium

1 cup artichoke hearts, rinsed, chopped

1 cup tomatoes, diced, salt-free

1 cup wild rice, uncooked

¼ cup onion, minced

2 tablespoons Kalamata olives, sliced • (optional)

1 tablespoon capers

1 teaspoon garlic, fresh, minced

½ teaspoon basil, dry

¼ teaspoon red pepper flakes

¼ teaspoon thyme, dry

Black pepper, freshly ground, to taste

Parsley, fresh, chopped

DIRECTIONS

1. Cook wild rice according to package instructions.

2. Meanwhile, heat pan on medium-high heat. Add onions and garlic, stirring until golden brown. Add half of the broth to pan to loosen onion and garlic.

3. Add remaining ingredients (minus the rice and parsley) and stir. Bring to a boil and reduce heat to medium, simmering for 8–10 minutes.

4. To serve, add wild rice to a bowl. Top with Puttanesca sauce and chopped fresh parsley.

Notes

This recipe is a variation of our Puttanesca sauce with the addition of chickpeas. Check our guidelines for Batch Cooking (page 89) for details.

Use fire-roasted diced tomatoes for a smokier variation.

Pappa Al Pomodoro (Bread and Tomato Soup)

Prep Time 10 min, Cook Time 30 min, Serves 2

INGREDIENTS

3 cups tomatoes, peeled, seeded, chopped

2 cups day-old crusty bread, crusts removed, cut into 1-inch cubes

2 cups water or vegetable broth, low-sodium

¼ cup onion, chopped

1 tablespoon basil, fresh, chopped

1 ½ teaspoon tomato paste

1 teaspoon garlic, fresh, minced

¼ teaspoon red pepper flakes (optional)

Black pepper, freshly ground, to taste

Sucanat or date sugar, to taste •

DIRECTIONS

1. Add onion to a large pot. Cook over medium-low heat about 5 minutes or until tender (stirring regularly and adding water or vegetable broth if sticking occurs).

2. Add garlic and cook about one minute.

3. Add tomatoes, tomato paste, red pepper flakes (if using), sucanat/date sugar, and freshly ground black pepper. Cook 10 minutes, stirring occasionally. More seasoning can be added, to taste.

4. Add bread cubes and stir, then add vegetable broth/water and ½ tablespoon basil. Simmer for 10 minutes or until the soup is thick, stirring regularly and mashing the bread.

5. Add ½ tablespoon basil and additional pepper or red pepper flakes to taste. Serve.

Notes

Gluten-free bread can be used as a substitute. Also, 14 ounces of canned tomatoes may be used in place of the fresh, ripe tomatoes.

78

Spaghetti Squash With Roasted Garlic and Tomatoes

Prep Time 15 min, Cook Time 45 min, Serves 2

INGREDIENTS

1 spaghetti squash

1 ½ cup vegetable broth, low-sodium

1 cup artichoke hearts, rinsed, chopped

1 cup tomatoes, diced, salt-free

½ cup onion, minced

1 Roasted Garlic clove, sliced (page 73)

2 tablespoons Kalamata olives, sliced • (optional)

1 tablespoon capers

½ teaspoon basil, dry

¼ teaspoon red pepper flakes

¼ teaspoon thyme, dry

Black pepper, freshly ground, to taste

DIRECTIONS

1. To prepare spaghetti squash, preheat oven to 400°F, then slice squash in half and scoop out the seeds. Place squash on a roasting pan with a little water to cover the bottom, then cook for 30–45 minutes or until tender.

2. Meanwhile, begin preparing the sauce by heating a pan on medium-high heat. Add onions stirring until golden brown. Add half of the broth to pan to loosen onion.

3. Add remaining ingredients and stir. Bring to a boil and then reduce heat to medium, simmering for 8–10 minutes.

4. Remove spaghetti squash from the oven and use a fork to pull the squash from the peel. Place in bowl and top with tomato sauce and sliced Roasted Garlic.

Notes

This recipe is a variation of our Puttanesca sauce. Check our guidelines for Batch Cooking (page 89) for details.

Use fire-roasted diced tomatoes for a smokier variation.

79

Vegan Shepherd's Pie

Prep Time 30 min, Cook Time 60 min, Serves 2

INGREDIENTS

4 cups potatoes, peeled, diced

2 cups vegetable broth, low-sodium

1 cup butternut squash, diced

1 cup chickpeas, cooked, rinsed

1 cup green peas

¾ cup carrots, diced

½ cup onion, sliced

¼ cup Homemade Nut Milk (page 14) or store-bought plant-based milk

2 tablespoons cornstarch

2 tablespoons nutritional yeast

2 tablespoons parsley, fresh, chopped

2 tablespoons tamari, low-sodium

2 tablespoons water

1 ¼ tablespoon tomato paste

1 ½ teaspoon miso paste, light

1 ½ teaspoon vegan Worcestershire

½ teaspoon garlic powder

½ teaspoon onion powder

½ teaspoon rosemary, fresh, chopped

DIRECTIONS

1. Preheat oven to 375°F.

2. In a Dutch oven (or large pot), caramelize sliced onion. Remove and roughly chop them. Put onion back in Dutch oven and add vegetable broth, garlic powder, onion powder, miso paste, vegan Worcester-shire, tamari, rosemary, and tomato paste and bring to a low simmer.

3. In a separate pot, bring potatoes and water to a boil. Cook until tender.

4. On a lined baking sheet, roast butternut squash until golden brown.

5. Bring water to boil. Add carrots and allow to cook until just tender (about 3 minutes). Remove carrots and set aside. Keep water. Add peas to boiling water and cook for about 2 minutes. Remove and add to carrots.

6. Combine cornstarch and water to create a slurry. Add slurry to onion mixture.

7. Add carrots, butternut squash and chickpeas to onion mixture. Continue to simmer.

8. For mashed potatoes, strain the boiled potatoes and return to the pot. Add nutritional yeast, chopped parsley and plant-based milk. Mash until smooth. (Add more plant-based milk if needed).

9. In a casserole dish, add vegetable mixture. Carefully add mashed potatoes on top until completely covered.

10. Turn on the broiler and cook until potatoes start to turn golden brown on top.

80

Drunken Noodles

Prep Time 10 min, Cook Time 30 min, Serves 2

INGREDIENTS

1 cup rice noodles, uncooked

¾ cup carrots, peeled, thinly sliced

¾ cup Roma tomatoes, chopped

½ cup green bell pepper, sliced

½ cup onion, sliced

½ cup orange bell pepper, sliced

½ cup Thai basil, fresh, chopped

3 tablespoons tamari, low-sodium

3 tablespoons vegetable broth, low-sodium

2 tablespoons sucanat •

1 tablespoon garlic powder

1 tablespoon hot sauce (more to taste)

1 tablespoon lime juice, freshly squeezed

1 tablespoon sesame seeds •

DIRECTIONS

1. Cook rice noodles according to package instructions.

2. In a large bowl, combine rice wine vinegar, tamari, vegetable broth, hot sauce, sucanat, lime juice and sesame seeds.

3. Add cooked noodles and fully coat with sauce. Set aside.

4. In a large sauté pan on medium-high, sauté onion, garlic powder and carrots.

5. Cover with a lid to steam. Sauté for a minute or two. Remove lid. Cook for 3 to 4 minutes, total. Add peppers, tomatoes and basil. Cook for 3 to 4 minutes.

6. Add sauce and noodle mixture and toss all together for a few more minutes until all flavors are combined.

81

Moroccan Tofu

Prep Time 10 min, Cook Time 50 min, Serves 2

INGREDIENTS

2 cups tomatoes, diced, salt-free

1 to 1 ½ cup couscous, cooked

1 cup tofu, firm, pressed
for 10 minutes

½ cup onion, diced

¼ cup apricots, dried, cut into strips •

¼ cup cranberries, dried •

2 tablespoons tamari, low-sodium

1 tablespoon apple cider vinegar

1 tablespoon miso paste, light

1 teaspoon garlic, fresh, minced

½ teaspoon dill, dry

½ teaspoon water

¼ teaspoon cinnamon, ground

¼ teaspoon cumin, ground

¼ teaspoon curry powder

¼ teaspoon garlic powder

¼ teaspoon smoked paprika

DIRECTIONS

1. Preheat oven to 400°F.

2. Line a baking sheet with parchment paper.

3. Cut tofu into 6 rectangles and place onto the sheet.

4. Mix miso paste, garlic powder and water together. Spread a thin layer on tofu. Set aside.

5. In a large Dutch oven, gently toast ground cinnamon, cumin, curry, and paprika. Continually stir with a wooden spoon making sure not to burn the spices. Once you smell the aromas of the spices, add onion, minced garlic, tomatoes, dried fruit, tamari, apple cider vinegar and dried dill. Continue to cook over low heat for 40 minutes.

6. At the 25-minute mark, cook tofu in the oven for 15 minutes. The edges should start turning light brown.

7. Place stewed tomatoes (Moroccan Sauce) in bowl then top with tofu.

8. Serve with ½ to ¾ cup cooked couscous per person.

Notes

For those with soy allergy or sensitivity, replace tofu with mushrooms, non-soy tempeh, or seitan.

Five Spice Cauliflower

Prep Time 20 min, Cook Time 45 min, Serves 2

INGREDIENTS

1 cup cauliflower florets

1 cup green beans

½ cup brown rice, uncooked

½ cup red bell pepper, julienned

1 ½ tablespoon tamari, low-sodium

1 tablespoon Dijon mustard

1 ½ teaspoon fermented
black bean paste

1 ½ teaspoon garlic, fresh, minced

1 ½ teaspoon ginger, fresh, minced

1 ½ teaspoon rice wine vinegar

½ teaspoon five spice

½ teaspoon hot sauce

DIRECTIONS

1. Preheat oven to 375°F.

2. In a bowl, mix together Dijon mustard, five spice, ½ tablespoon tamari, and rice wine vinegar.

3. Massage marinade into cauliflower.

4. Place cauliflower onto a baking sheet lined with parchment paper. Cook for 25 minutes or until cauliflower is tender and light brown.

5. Trim the beans, cut on the diagonal.

6. Bring water to boil. Cook beans for 2 to 3 minutes until just tender. Drain and rinse under cold water. Set aside.

7. Heat a large sauté pan over high heat. Add green beans and red bell pepper and cook 3–5 minutes. Add garlic and ginger. Continue to stir and reduce heat or garlic will burn easily.

8. Just before serving, stir black bean paste and 1 tablespoon tamari.

9. Cook rice according to package instructions.

10. Add rice, cauliflower and beans to individual bowls to serve.

Vegetable Coconut Curry

Prep Time 15 min, Cook Time 30 min, Serves 2

INGREDIENTS

1 cup chickpeas, cooked, rinsed

1 cup coconut milk, low-fat •

1 cup potatoes, peeled, diced

1 cup yam, peeled, diced

½ cup brown rice, uncooked

½ cup green peas, frozen, thawed

2 tablespoons cashews, chopped •

1 tablespoon curry powder
(plus extra for potatoes and yams)

1 tablespoon miso paste, light

1 tablespoon tamari, low-sodium

1 ½ teaspoon garlic powder
(plus extra for potatoes and yams)

Red pepper flakes, to taste

DIRECTIONS

1. Place curry powder in a medium-sized pot. Over low heat, slowly roast curry powder. Make sure to keep powder moving with a spoon so that it roasts and does not burn. Cook for 1 to 2 minutes.

2. Turn off heat and whisk coconut milk into the pan. Add miso paste and cook over the lowest burner setting.

3. Set up steamer. Season potatoes with a few shakes of curry powder and garlic powder; steam them until just tender. Once cooked, add to coconut curry sauce.

4. Season yams with curry powder and garlic powder. Steam yams until just tender. Remove from the steamer and place on a plate and allow to cool.

5. Cook rice according to package directions.

6. Once potatoes are soft and sauce is starting to thicken, turn off the heat.

7. In a large sauté pan, add yams, cashews, chickpeas, and peas. Cook over medium-high heat. Add garlic powder and tamari. Continue to stir until well coated. Remove from heat.

8. Place rice on a plate, then top with coconut curry sauce and potatoes. Finish with yams and peas.

Mango Cauliflower Stir Fry

Prep Time 15 min, Cook Time 30 min, Serves 2

INGREDIENTS

1 ½ cup baby spinach

1 cup cauliflower florets

1 cup chickpeas, cooked, rinsed

1 cup mango

¾ cup lentils, uncooked

½ cup onion, sliced

2 tablespoons parsley, fresh, chopped

1 tablespoon green chili, chopped

1 tablespoon lime juice,
freshly squeezed

1 tablespoon mint, fresh, chopped

1 tablespoon rice wine vinegar

1 tablespoon tamari, low-sodium

1 tablespoon water

½ teaspoon curry powder

¼ teaspoon cumin, ground

DIRECTIONS

1. Bring water to boil. Cook cauliflower until just tender. Remove from water and place cauliflower on a baking sheet to allow it to fully dry and cool. Cauliflower will continue to cook with onions, so avoid overcooking.

2. Heat a large sauté pan over high heat. Add onions, stirring for 1 minute. As onions start to release liquid, reduce heat and add spices. Continue to stir and cook until onions start to caramelize.

3. Drain and rinse chickpeas. Add to onions along with green chilies, cooking for 5 minutes.

4. At this point, add cauliflower to onions and chickpeas.

5. Peel mango and cut into a large dice.

6. Combine tamari, water, lime juice, and rice wine vinegar.

7. Cook lentils according to package instructions.

8. Add mango and tamari to sauté pan. Fold spinach into the mixture, cooking until just starts to wilt.

9. Place lentils in a bowl and top with mango cauliflower stir fry.

85

Soba Noodles With BBQ Tofu and Vegetables in Peanut Sauce

Prep Time 15 min, Cook Time 45 min, Serves 2

INGREDIENTS

BBQ Tofu

1 cup broccoli

1 cup tofu, firm

¾ cup soba noodles, uncooked

1 tablespoon peanuts, roasted, oil-free, salt-free, chopped •

2 teaspoons hot sauce

1 ½ teaspoon miso paste, light

1 ½ teaspoon tamari, low-sodium

1 ½ teaspoon teriyaki BBQ sauce

¼ teaspoon garlic powder

¼ teaspoon onion powder

Peanut Sauce

2 tablespoons peanut butter, roasted, oil-free, salt-free •

2 tablespoons water

1 tablespoon lime juice, freshly squeezed

1 tablespoon rice wine vinegar

1 tablespoon tamari, low-sodium

½ teaspoon hot sauce

½ teaspoon vegan Worcestershire

DIRECTIONS

1. Preheat oven to 375°F.

2. For tofu marinade, mix miso, tamari and hot sauce.

3. Cut tofu into strips or cubes, then toss with marinade to coat.

4. Put tofu on a lined baking sheet and place in oven, cooking for 15 to 20 minutes until tofu turns light brown.

5. Make Peanut Sauce by combining all ingredients in a large mixing bowl and whisking together. If it is too thick, you can add more water to thin.

6. Cut broccoli and steam for 3 to 5 minutes. Remove from steamer and place on a lined baking sheet. Sprinkle with garlic powder, onion powder, BBQ sauce and peanuts.

7. Place in oven, cooking until the edges of the broccoli start to crisp.

8. Cook soba noodles according to package instructions.

9. Remove from water and toss in the Peanut Sauce. Add veggies and tofu, and serve.

Notes

For those with peanut allergies, replace peanut butter with another nut butter or sunflower seed butter and whole peanuts with roasted cashews or sunflower seeds.

For those with soy allergy or sensitivity, replace tofu with mushrooms, non-soy tempeh, or seitan.

Bulgur and Lentil Pilaf With Leeks

Prep Time 15 min, Cook Time 35 min, Serves 2

INGREDIENTS

1 ½ cup water

1 ⅓ cup leafy green vegetables (e.g. chard, kale, mustard, spinach) (optional)

½ cup leeks, chopped (white and light green parts only)

⅓ cup lentils, uncooked

¼ cup bulgur, uncooked

1 bay leaf

1 teaspoon garlic, fresh, minced

½ teaspoon cumin, ground

Cayenne pepper, to taste

DIRECTIONS

1. Place lentils in a bowl and add warm water to cover by one inch.

2. As lentils are soaking, clean and halve the leek, then cut it into thin crosswise slices.

3. Heat a large pot over medium-high heat. Add leeks and cook 5 to 10 minutes until crispy. Set half of them aside for garnishing.

4. Keep half leeks in the pot, add garlic and cook for 15 seconds. Add bulgur and cook for 2 minutes, then add cumin and cayenne and cook for 30 seconds.

5. Drain lentils and add them to pot. Add 1 ½ cup water and the bay leaf. Bring to a simmer, cover and cook for 15 minutes.

6. If using leafy green vegetables, rinse and add them to the pot, cooking 5 more minutes before serving.

7. Transfer lentil and bulgur to serving dish and top with reserved leeks.

Notes

This is a versatile recipe that allows a few variations. For example, long-grain rice can be used instead of bulgur, caramelized onions can replace leeks, and the dish can be served with dairy-free plain yogurt.

Resources

Advance Preparation and Batch Cooking

WEEK 1 | ADVANCE PREPARATION

1. **Baked Potatoes** — Cook ahead of time and reheat when needed.

2. **Cashew Sour Cream** (optional) — Prepare and store to serve with Baked Potato, Black Bean Burrito, Black Bean Chili, and/or Southwestern Sweet Potato Chips.

3. **Dry Ingredients** — Measure, prepare and store seasoning mix for Wholesome Power Wedges and/or dry ingredients for any of the breakfast options.

4. **Mushroom Gravy** — Prepare and store to serve with Baked Potato and/or Steamed Broccoli.

5. **Raw Vegetables** — Wash and cut up asparagus, artichoke bottoms, bell peppers, cabbage, leeks, onions and/or any other vegetables needed during the week. Store them in glass containers in the refrigerator.

6. **Salad Dressings and Sauces** — Select, prepare, and store oil-free plant-based salad dressings and sauces to be used during the week.

7. **Spreads** — Select, prepare and store hummus variations and/or any other spreads to be used during the week.

8. **Tofu** — Press and marinate tofu ahead of preparing Baked Tofu.

WEEK 1 | BATCH COOKING

1. **Black Beans** — Use the How to Cook Dried Beans directions (page 92) to cook black beans for black beans for Black Bean Chili, Black Bean Burrito, Spicy Black Bean and Corn Salad, Southwestern Sweet Potato Chips and Yummy Black Bean, Beet, and Shiitake Burgers.

2. **Brown Rice** — Cook amount necessary to make Black Bean Burrito, Mango Fried Rice, Roasted Rice and Kale Stuffed Peppers, and Yummy Black Bean, Beet, and Shiitake Burgers.

3. **Chickpeas** — Use the How to Cook Dried Beans directions (page 92) to cook chickpeas for optional breakfast/snack Hummus spread, Hummus Veggie Tortilla Pizzas and Hummus Veggie Wrap.

4. **Yummy Black Bean, Beet, and Shiitake Burgers** — Prepare and freeze patties ahead of time. Brown rice (from batch cooking) can be used instead of forbidden rice. Store-bought oil-free veggie burgers can also be used instead of homemade patties.

89

Advance Preparation and Batch Cooking

WEEK 2 | ADVANCE PREPARATION

1. **Cashew Cream Sauce** — Prepare and store for Un-Tuna Sandwich.

2. **Dry Ingredients** — Measure, mix and store dry ingredients for any of the breakfast options.

3. **Raw Vegetables** — Wash and cut up acorn squash, Brussels sprouts, bell peppers, green onions, onions, zucchini and/or any other vegetables needed during the week. Store them in glass containers in the refrigerator.

4. **Salad Dressings and Sauces** — Select, prepare and store oil-free plant-based salad dressings and sauces to be used during the week.

5. **Spaghetti Squash** — Bake it ahead of time and reheat to serve with Puttanesca.

6. **Spreads** — Select, prepare, and store hummus variations and/or any other spreads to be used during the week.

WEEK 2 | BATCH COOKING

1. **Chickpeas** — Use the How to Cook Dried Beans directions (page 92) to cook chickpeas for optional breakfast/snack Hummus spread, Chickpeas and Tomato Stew, Un-Tuna Sandwich, Kale and Chickpea Salad, Wild Rice With Chickpeas, and Vegan Shepherd's Pie.

2. **Puttanesca Sauce** — Cook amount necessary to make Chickpeas and Tomato Stew, Fusilli alla Puttanesca, Spaghetti Squash With Roasted Garlic and Tomatoes, and Wild Rice With Chickpeas. Half of the sauce will be used as-is while the remaining will have chickpeas. Simmer Puttanesca sauce longer when preparing Fusilli, Spaghetti Squash and/or Wild Rice to allow excess liquid to evaporate.

3. **Roasted Garlic** — Prepare, make and store for use in Roasted Garlic Mashed Cauliflower, Spaghetti Squash With Roasted Garlic and Tomatoes and optional breakfast Sweet Potato Hash.

4. **Wild Rice** — Cook amount necessary to make Wild Rice and Chickpeas.

Advance Preparation and Batch Cooking

WEEK 3 | ADVANCE PREPARATION

1. **Dry Ingredients** — Measure, mix and store dry ingredients for any of the breakfast options.

2. **Raw Vegetables** — Wash and cut up bell peppers, cabbage, carrots, kale, leeks, mint, green onions, onions, parsley, and/or any other vegetables needed during the week. Store them in glass containers in the refrigerator.

3. **Salad Dressings and Sauces** — Select, prepare and store oil-free plant-based salad dressings and sauces to be used during the week.

4. **Spreads** — Select, prepare and store hummus variations and/or any other spreads to be used during the week.

5. **Tofu** — Press and marinate tofu ahead of preparing Banh Mi Bowl, Baked Tofu, Moroccan Tofu, Soba Noodles With BBQ Tofu and Vegetables, Spicy Peanut Tofu Lettuce Wraps, and Vietnamese-Style Spring Rolls.

WEEK 3 | BATCH COOKING

1. **Brown Rice** — Cook amount necessary to make Banh Mi Bowl, Five Spice Cauliflower, and Vegetable Coconut Curry.

2. **Chickpeas** — Use the How to Cook Dried Beans directions (page 92) to cook chickpeas for Baked Falafel, Mango Cauliflower Stir Fry, Turkish Chickpea Salad, Vegetable Coconut Curry, and/or optional breakfast/snack Hummus spread.

3. **Lentil** — Cook amount necessary to make Mango Cauliflower Stir Fry.

How to Cook Dried Beans

Prep Time 5 min, Cook Time 120 min, Makes 5 cups

INGREDIENTS

10 cups water

3 cups beans, dry (e.g. black, kidney, pinto, chickpeas)

2 cups onion, roughly chopped

3 tablespoons garlic, fresh, minced

1 teaspoon cumin, ground

1 teaspoon oregano, dry

Red pepper flakes, to taste

DIRECTIONS

1. Sort the beans, checking for rocks and dirt, then rinse and place in a large pot.
2. Cover with fresh water (approximately 10 cups of water per pound) and bring to a boil over high heat.
3. Reduce the heat to a low simmer. Skim off any foam.
4. Stir in the onion, garlic, oregano, cumin, and red pepper flakes.
5. Keep an eye on your beans, stirring occasionally. The beans are done when they are tender all the way through but still firm and intact, about an hour and a half.

Notes

Cooking time may vary depending on the age of the beans.

Oil-Free Salad Dressing Recipes

Almond Chili

Prep Time 10 min, Cook Time 0 min, Serves 2

INGREDIENTS

3 tablespoons water

2 tablespoons almond butter •

1 tablespoon lemon juice,
freshly squeezed

1 tablespoon maple syrup •

1 tablespoon tamari, low-sodium

1 ½ teaspoon rice vinegar

½ teaspoon garlic, fresh, minced

¼ teaspoon serrano pepper,
chopped (optional)

DIRECTIONS

1. Blend all ingredients in a small blender or food processor until smooth and creamy. Keep it in the refrigerator for up to a week.

94

Asian

Prep Time 5 min, Cook Time 0 min, Serves 2

INGREDIENTS

1 tablespoon water

1 ½ teaspoon green onions
(green parts), chopped

1 ½ teaspoon lime juice, freshly squeezed

1 ½ teaspoon rice wine vinegar

½ teaspoon maple syrup •

½ teaspoon tamari, low-sodium

Ginger, fresh, minced, to taste

Turmeric, ground, to taste

DIRECTIONS

1. Add all ingredients to a small mixing bowl and whisk.

Avocado

Prep Time 5 min, Cook Time 0 min, Serves 2

INGREDIENTS

¼ avocado, ripe •

Lemon or lime juice, freshly squeezed

DIRECTIONS

1. Massage avocado into salad greens before other vegetables are added, then top with a squeeze of lemon or lime.

Notes

This works best on thicker-textured greens like kale or romaine lettuce.

Basic Balsamic

Prep Time 5 min, Cook Time 0 min, Serves 2

INGREDIENTS

1 tablespoon balsamic vinegar

1 tablespoon water

½ teaspoon Dijon mustard

Garlic powder, to taste

Smoked paprika, to taste

DIRECTIONS

1. Add all ingredients to a small mixing bowl and whisk.

Basil Tahini

Prep Time 5 min, Cook Time 0 min, Serves 2

INGREDIENTS

¼ cup apple cider vinegar

2 tablespoons tahini •

2 tablespoons tamari, low-sodium

1 ½ teaspoon garlic, fresh, minced

½ teaspoon basil, fresh

DIRECTIONS

1. Combine vinegar, tamari, tahini, garlic, and basil in a blender and blend until smooth.

Cashew Curry

Prep Time 5 min, Cook Time 0 min, Serves 2

INGREDIENTS

3 tablespoons cashews, raw, unsalted •

3 tablespoons water

1 ½ tablespoon orange juice, freshly squeezed

½ teaspoon garlic, fresh, minced

¼ teaspoon curry powder

DIRECTIONS

1. Place dressing ingredients into a blender and set aside so that cashews can soften.

2. Blend dressing ingredients until smooth. Stir the orange zest into the blended dressing and transfer to a glass container (no additional blending).

3. Store it in the refrigerator.

Cilantro Lime Vinaigrette

Prep Time 10 min, Cook Time 0 min, Serves 2

INGREDIENTS

2 tablespoons lime juice, freshly squeezed

1 tablespoon cilantro, fresh, chopped

½ teaspoon garlic, fresh, minced

½ teaspoon maple syrup •

Black pepper, freshly ground, to taste

DIRECTIONS

1. Add ingredients to a food processor and pulse for 15–30 seconds until combined.

Citrus

Prep Time 5 min, Cook Time 0 min, Serves 2

INGREDIENTS

1 lime or lemon

DIRECTIONS

1. Put a generous squeeze of fresh lemon or lime juice all over your salad right before serving.

Notes

This method works best on smaller, individually served salads.

Fresh Basil

Prep Time 5 min, Cook Time 0 min, Serves 2

INGREDIENTS

2 tablespoons basil, fresh

1 ½ tablespoon balsamic vinegar

1 ½ tablespoon lemon juice, freshly squeezed

1 teaspoon garlic, fresh, minced

1 teaspoon lemon zest

Black pepper, freshly ground, to taste

DIRECTIONS

1. Process lemon zest, lemon juice, balsamic vinegar, garlic and black pepper in a blender or food processor until smooth.
2. Add basil and pulse 5 or 6 times until well blended.

Greek

Prep Time 5 min, Cook Time 0 min, Serves 2

INGREDIENTS

1 tablespoon water

1 ½ teaspoon tahini •

½ teaspoon Dijon mustard

½ teaspoon lemon or lime juice, freshly squeezed

DIRECTIONS

1. Add all ingredients to a small mixing bowl and whisk.

Italian

Prep Time 5 min, Cook Time 0 min, Serves 2

INGREDIENTS

2 tablespoons basil, fresh, chopped

2 tablespoons hummus, oil-free

1 tablespoon Dijon mustard

1 tablespoon red wine vinegar

DIRECTIONS

1. Add all ingredients to a small mixing bowl and whisk. If needed, add a few teaspoons water to thin.

Low-Fat Italian

Prep Time 5 min, Cook Time 0 min, Serves 2

INGREDIENTS

1 tablespoon apple cider vinegar

1 tablespoon water

½ teaspoon Dijon mustard

¼ teaspoon agave or maple syrup •

Oregano, dry, to taste

Thyme, dry, to taste

DIRECTIONS

1. Add all ingredients to a small mixing bowl and whisk. Allow to rest 5–10 minutes before adding to your salad.

Maple Tahini

Prep Time 5 min, Cook Time 0 min, Serves 2

INGREDIENTS

1 tablespoon tahini •

1 ½ teaspoon apple cider vinegar

1 ½ teaspoon maple syrup •

1 ½ teaspoon water

1 teaspoon lemon juice, freshly squeezed

Black pepper, freshly ground, to taste

Cayenne pepper, to taste

DIRECTIONS

1. Whisk all ingredients in a small mixing bowl until smooth and creamy. Keep it in the refrigerator for up to a week.

Mediterranean

Prep Time 5 min, Cook Time 0 min, Serves 2

INGREDIENTS

1 tablespoon water

1 ½ teaspoon hummus, oil-free

½ teaspoon lemon or lime juice, freshly squeezed

¼ to ½ teaspoon agave or maple syrup •

DIRECTIONS

1. Add all ingredients to a small mixing bowl and whisk.

Mexican

Prep Time 0 min, Cook Time 0 min, Serves 2

INGREDIENTS

1 to 1 ½ tablespoon of your favorite salsa

DIRECTIONS

1. Add directly to your salad before serving.

Miso Sesame Ginger

Prep Time 5 min, Cook Time 0 min, Serves 2

INGREDIENTS

¼ cup warm water

2 tablespoons miso paste, light

2 tablespoons rice vinegar

2 tablespoons tamari, low-sodium

1 tablespoon mirin

1 ½ teaspoon red pepper flakes (optional)

¼ teaspoon garlic, fresh, minced

¼ teaspoon ginger, fresh, minced

Black pepper, freshly ground, to taste

DIRECTIONS

1. Combine all ingredients in mixer and pulse until smooth.

Mustard Garlic Vinaigrette

Prep Time 5 min, Cook Time 0 min, Serves 2

INGREDIENTS

2 tablespoons Dijon mustard

2 teaspoons red wine vinegar

1 ¼ teaspoon smoked paprika

¾ teaspoon garlic, fresh, minced

Black pepper, freshly ground, to taste

DIRECTIONS

1. Combine ingredients in a small bowl and mix thoroughly.

....

Orange

Prep Time 5 min, Cook Time 0 min, Serves 2

INGREDIENTS

1 orange, juiced

1 ½ teaspoon orange zest

1 ½ teaspoon white wine vinegar

½ teaspoon Dijon mustard

Black pepper, freshly ground, to taste

DIRECTIONS

1. Combine orange juice, orange zest, mustard and vinegar in a large salad bowl and stir well with a whisk.

2. Season with black pepper.

....

Smoky Citrus

Prep Time 5 min, Cook Time 0 min, Serves 2

INGREDIENTS

½ lemon, juiced, zested

¼ cup cashews, soaked •

¼ cup water

2 tablespoons Medjool dates, pitted, chopped •

2 tablespoons silken tofu

1 ½ teaspoon apple cider vinegar

1 ½ teaspoon miso paste, light

½ teaspoon cumin, ground

½ teaspoon smoked paprika

DIRECTIONS

1. Add all ingredients to a blender and blend until smooth.

Sweet and Spicy Asian

Prep Time 5 min, Cook Time 0 min, Serves 2

INGREDIENTS

1 to 2 tablespoons water

1 tablespoon flaxseed meal •

1 tablespoon rice vinegar

1 tablespoon tamari, low-sodium

1 ½ teaspoon lime juice,
freshly squeezed

1 teaspoon hot sauce

1 teaspoon maple syrup •

¼ teaspoon garlic powder

¼ teaspoon ginger, fresh, minced

DIRECTIONS

1. Mix all ingredients together and allow to sit, giving the flaxseed meal time to hydrate and thicken.

Sweet Raspberry

Prep Time 5 min, Cook Time 0 min, Serves 2

INGREDIENTS

1 tablespoon apple cider vinegar

1 tablespoon water

½ to 1 teaspoon raspberry preserve

DIRECTIONS

1. Add all ingredients to a small mixing bowl and whisk.

Tahini

Prep Time 5 min, Cook Time 0 min, Serves 2

INGREDIENTS

2 tablespoons tahini •

2 tablespoons water

1 ½ teaspoon lemon juice,
freshly squeezed (optional)

½ teaspoon garlic powder (optional)

DIRECTIONS

1. Whisk all ingredients in a small bowl until smooth.

Waldorf

Prep Time 5 min, Cook Time 0 min, Serves 2

INGREDIENTS

1 lemon, juiced, zested

½ cup cashews, soaked •

½ cup water

⅓ cup silken tofu

2 tablespoons Medjool dates, pitted, chopped •

1 tablespoon apple cider vinegar

1 tablespoon miso paste, light

DIRECTIONS

1. Add all ingredients into a blender and blend until smooth.

2. Transfer to a container and store it in the refrigerator.

Author

ROSANE OLIVEIRA, DVM, PhD

Rosane Oliveira, DVM, PhD is Founding Director of the Integrative Medicine program and Adjunct Assistant Professor of Public Health Sciences at the School of Medicine at the University of California Davis.

She has over 20 years of scientific experience in genetic research with a special interest in nutritional genomics, which explores the interplay between diet and genes and investigates how nutrition influences health and longevity.

She is the creator of Bite-Sized, a new program designed to teach people how to implement lasting habit change. She also writes about health and nutrition every week on UC Davis Integrative Medicine's popular blog and teaches lifestyle medicine to medical students at UC Davis.

Dr. Oliveira became a vegetarian in 1988 and has followed a whole food, plant-based diet since 2008. She is a native of Rio de Janeiro, Brazil and has lived in the US since 2003 and in Davis, California since 2011.

CHEF STEFEN JANKE (CONTRIBUTOR)

Stephen Janke is a chef and co-owner of Jule's Foods and Plant Punk Kitchen.

He began his career at the California Culinary Academy in San Francisco and has spent over 20 years working first at prestigious kitchens in San Francisco (Aqua) and Los Angeles (Patina), then as a private chef in Los Angeles.

Chef Janke and his wife Julie ran a successful catering business for 17 years. They transitioned to a whole food, plant-based diet after Julie's diagnosis of stage 4 colorectal cancer in 2014. They now share plant-based recipes and products through Jule's Foods, their new venture featuring Cashew Brie varieties.

Recipes: Asian Chop Salad, Banh Mi Bowl, Chocolate Ginger Chia Pudding, Classic Hummus, Cocoa Spiced Quinoa Breakfast Bowl, Creamy Steel-Cut Oatmeal, Drunken Noodles, Five-Spice Cauliflower, Fluffy Vegan Pancakes, Italian Salad, Mango Cauliflower Stir Fry, Moroccan Tofu, Oil-Free Salad Dressings, Roasted Breakfast Potatoes, Slaw Salad, Soba Noodle With BBQ Tofu and Vegetables in Peanut Sauce, Tofu Scramble, Un-Tuna Sandwich, Vegan Shepherd's Pie, Vegetable Coconut Curry, Vegetable Lasagna Rolls, Waldorf Salad

Index

Index

Index

H

I

J

K

L

Index

N

O

Index

Q

QUINOA

R

RADICCHIO

RADISH

RAISIN

RED CABBAGE AND AVOCADO SALAD, 47

RICE

ROASTED BREAKFAST POTATOES, 22

ROASTED GARLIC MASHED CAULIFLOWER, 73

ROASTED GARLIC, 73

ROASTED RICE AND KALE STUFFED PEPPERS, 32

ROASTED VEGGIE SALAD, 29

S

SALSA

SAUTÉED BRUSSELS SPROUTS, 67

SAUTÉED SPINACH, 41

SEED

SHALLOT

SLAW SALAD, 26

Index

Are Your Unhealthy Habits Holding You Back?

Join Our Bite-Sized Community to Get All the Tools, Resources and Support You Need — One Bite at a Time

 bite-sized

bite-sized.com/amazon

Made in the USA
Columbia, SC
15 April 2020